G000113887

THE TIMES TOP 100 GRADUATE EMPLOYERS

The definitive guide to the leading employers recruiting graduates during 2010-2011.

HIGH FLIERS

HIGH FLIERS PUBLICATIONS LTD
IN ASSOCIATION WITH THE TIMES

Published by High Fliers Publications Limited
King's Gate, 1 Bravingtons Walk, London N1 9AE
Telephone: 020 7428 9100   Web: www.Top100GraduateEmployers.com

Editor Martin Birchall
Publisher Gill Thomas
Production Manager Robin Burrows
Portrait Photography Sarah Merson

Copyright © 2010 High Fliers Publications Limited

All rights reserved. Without limiting the rights under copyright reserved
above, no part of this publication may be reproduced, stored in or
introduced into a retrieval system, or transmitted, in any form or by any
means (electronic, mechanical, photocopying, recording or otherwise),
without the prior written permission of the publisher of this book.

The Times Top 100 Graduate Employers is based on research results
from The UK Graduate Careers Survey 2010, produced by High Fliers
Research Ltd.

The greatest care has been taken in compiling this book. However, no
responsibility can be accepted by the publishers or compilers for the
accuracy of the information presented.

Where opinion is expressed it is that of the author or advertiser and
does not necessarily coincide with the editorial views of High Fliers
Publications Limited or The Times newspaper.

Printed and bound in Italy by L.E.G.O. S.p.A.

A CIP catalogue record for this book
is available from the British Library.
ISBN 978-0-9559257-1-9

Contents

Information Request Service

Find out more about Britain's top employers and you could start your career £5,000 richer or win a £50 iTunes voucher or a copy of *The Graduate Jobs Formula* book.

Foreword

by Martin Birchall
Editor, The Times Top 100 Graduate Employers

Welcome to the latest edition of *The Times Top 100 Graduate Employers*, your guide to the UK's leading employers who are recruiting graduates in 2010-2011.

In many ways, 2010 has been a year of dramatic new beginnings. The Conservative-Liberal Democrat coalition has ushered in a new approach to Government, the UK economy has emerged from the deepest recession for more than fifty years and the country is facing-up to a new era of austerity and public spending cuts.

For the graduate employment market, 2010 marked an important turning point too. After two years of swingeing cuts to graduate recruitment when more than a quarter of entry-level vacancies at the country's best-known and most sought-after employers were cancelled or postponed, the number of graduate jobs on offer to the 'Class of 2010' increased sharply, restoring around half of the positions lost during the recession.

One of the reasons that the graduate job market is starting to recover is that the vast majority of major national and international employers continued to recruit graduates throughout the recession, albeit in sometimes greatly reduced numbers compared with the bumper recruitment levels of 2006 and 2007.

For most of these organisations, hiring new graduates has always been about developing a steady supply of future managers and leaders for their organisation, rather than simply filling immediate vacancies. Very few top employers were keen to break this essential talent pipeline and so, irrespective of the worsening economic conditions, the vast majority of organisations opted not to shut down their graduate programmes and have maintained some form of recruitment during the recession.

Despite this, the downturn in the graduate job market has had a profound effect on recent graduates. More than 10 per cent of those who left university in the 'Class of 2009' were unemployed six months after graduation and tens of thousands of those who did find work were employed in non-graduate roles. The final destinations of a further fifty thousand graduates were unknown. Inevitably, the competition for places on the top graduate schemes has been ferocious in both 2009 and 2010.

If you're one of the 325,000 final year university students due to graduate in the summer of 2011, then the outlook is more encouraging. Recruiters featured within this edition of *The Times Top 100 Graduate Employers* expect to increase their graduate intake by a further 6.8 per cent during the 2010-2011 recruitment season.

Nationally, an estimated five thousand employers are preparing to recruit graduates in the year ahead and more than six hundred organisations have already confirmed that they will be holding recruitment events on campus. With such a wide choice of different types of employment and graduate jobs, how then can prospective employers be assessed and ranked?

To find out, we interviewed over 16,000 final year students who graduated from universities across the UK in the summer of 2010, and asked them "Which employer do you think offers the best opportunities for graduates?". Between them, the 'Class of 2010' named organisations in every imaginable employment sector – from the country's best-known retailers to the 'Big Four' accounting & professional services firms, government departments to charities, high street banks to consulting firms and leading IT companies. The one hundred employers who were mentioned most often during the research form *The Times Top 100 Graduate Employers*.

This book is therefore a celebration of the employers who are judged to offer the brightest

prospects for graduates. Whether by the perceived quality of their training programmes, the business success that they enjoy, the scale of their organisations, or by the impression that their recruitment promotions have made – these are the employers that are most attractive to university-leavers in 2010.

The Times Top 100 Graduate Employers will not necessarily identify which organisation is right for you: only you can decide that. But it is an invaluable reference if you want to discover what Britain's leading employers have to offer new graduates.

Leaving university and finding your first job can be a daunting process but it is one of the most important steps you'll ever take. Having a good understanding of the range of opportunities available must be the best way to start.

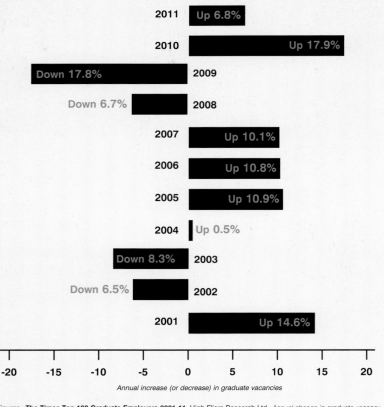

How Graduate Vacancies have Changed at Britain's Leading Employers 2001-2011

2011	Up 6.8%
2010	Up 17.9%
2009	Down 17.8%
2008	Down 6.7%
2007	Up 10.1%
2006	Up 10.8%
2005	Up 10.9%
2004	Up 0.5%
2003	Down 8.3%
2002	Down 6.5%
2001	Up 14.6%

Annual increase (or decrease) in graduate vacancies

Source **The Times Top 100 Graduate Employers 2001-11**, High Fliers Research Ltd. Annual change in graduate vacancy levels at the organisations featured in The Times Top 100 Graduate Employers in 2001-2011

Which company offers 'the most generous graduate package' according to The Times Top 100 Graduate Employers 2009 - 2010?*

B) KPMG

C) Ernst & Young

Think the biggest pay-packets are in the City? Don't bank on it. Think all the money's in consultancy? Here's some free advice. Aldi offers a benefits package that's second to none. But, we'll expect you to earn every penny of it. So, you'll hit the ground running. And within twelve months, you'll be managing four to six Aldi stores - in effect, running your own multi-million pound business. Of course, a career with Aldi isn't for everyone. You'll need to be a self-starter, tenacious, and have vast reserves of drive and determination to draw on when the going gets tough. But, it'll be worth it – we guarantee that. Because at Aldi, you can get further, faster and enjoy levels of responsibility unheard of in other companies in such a short timeframe. So forget multiple choice, just make the right choice and go to **www.aldirecruitment.co.uk**

Graduate
Area Manager
£40,000

rising to
£61,000
after three years

Fully expensed
Audi A4

Opportunity
for directorship
within 5 years

International
secondment
opportunities

*The Times Top 100 Graduate Employers 2009 – 2010
Martin Birchall Managing Director, High Fliers Research: Understanding the Graduate Market - Page 28
"The most generous graduate package on offer in 2010 is Aldi's – they're providing new recruits with a
starting salary of £40,000 as well as a fully-expensed Audi A4 car."

No bull.

Straight talking from KPMG.

Graduate Programmes – All degree disciplines

We close for applications once we are full. To secure a place at KPMG, be sure to apply early. To find out more head straight to:

www.kpmg.co.uk/careers

AUDIT ■ TAX ■ ADVISORY

KPMG

Compiling the Top 100 Graduate Employers

by Gill Thomas
Publisher, High Fliers Publications Ltd

With the worst of the recession in Britain now over, there are signs that graduate recruitment is recovering and that the prospects for university-leavers are starting to improve – an estimated five thousand employers will be hiring graduates from UK universities during the 2010-2011 recruitment season.

With such a wide choice of employment to consider, selecting the organisation that is 'right' for you can be quite a challenge. How can you evaluate the different opportunities and decide which employers offer the best career paths? What basis can you use to assess so many different organisations and jobs?

It's clear there are no simple answers to these questions and no single individual employer can ever hope to be right for every graduate – everyone makes their own judgement about the organisations they want to work for and the type of job they find the most attractive.

How then can anyone produce a meaningful league table of Britain's leading graduate employers? What criteria can define whether one organisation is 'better' than another? To compile *The Times Top 100 Graduate Employers*, the independent market research company, High Fliers Research, interviewed 16,114 final year students who left UK universities in the summer of 2010.

These students from the 'Class of 2010' who took part in the study were selected at random to represent the full cross-section of finalists at their universities, not just those who had already secured graduate employment. The research examined students' experiences during their search for a graduate job and asked them about their attitudes to employers.

The key question used to produce the *Top 100* was "Which employer do you think offers the best opportunities for graduates?" This question was deliberately open-ended and students were not prompted in any way. Across the whole survey, finalists mentioned more than 800 different organisations – from the smallest local employers, to some of the world's best-known companies. The responses were analysed to identify the number of times each employer was mentioned. The one hundred organisations that were mentioned most often are the *The Times Top 100 Graduate Employers* for 2010.

Looking at the considerable selection of answers given by finalists from the 'Class of 2010' it is clear that individual students used very different criteria to determine which employer they considered offered the best opportunities for graduates. Some focused on employers' general reputations – their public image, their business profile or their commercial success. Others evaluated employers based on the information they had seen during their job search – the quality of recruitment promotions, the impression formed from meeting employers' representatives,

THE TIMES TOP 100 GRADUATE EMPLOYERS

The Top 100 Graduate Employers 2010

This Year	Last Year		This Year	Last Year	
1.	1	PricewaterhouseCoopers	51.	52	WPP
2.	2	Deloitte	52.	37	Atkins
3.	4	Civil Service	53.	44	RAF
4.	5	KPMG	54.	89	Lidl
5.	3	Aldi	55.	48	Citi
6.	6	NHS	56.	73	Bank of America Merrill Lynch
7.	8	Teach First	57.	40	Foreign Office
8.	7	Accenture	58.	62	The Co-operative Group
9.	9	BBC	59.	55	ExxonMobil
10.	10	Ernst & Young	60.	75	Boots
11.	11	Army	61.	88	AstraZeneca
12.	13	Procter & Gamble	62.	64	Herbert Smith
13.	17	Tesco	63.	71	Transport for London
14.	15	GlaxoSmithKline	64.	72	nucleargraduates
15.	19	Goldman Sachs	65.	76	Network Rail
16.	14	HSBC	66.	78	Bloomberg
17.	35	Barclays Bank	67.	43	Deutsche Bank
18.	16	BP	68.	99	Grant Thornton
19.	18	IBM	69.	NEW	Balfour Beatty
20.	23	L'Oréal	70.	66	Ministry of Defence
21.	28	Marks & Spencer	71.	70	Oxfam
22.	24	J.P. Morgan	72.	25	BT
23.	12	Shell	73.	80	Boston Consulting Group
24.	30	Allen & Overy	74.	94	Credit Suisse
25.	20	Google	75.	57	Arcadia Group
26.	21	Rolls-Royce	76.	77	Airbus
27.	32	Unilever	77.	54	Freshfields Bruckhaus Deringer
28.	45	John Lewis Partnership	78.	61	Lovells
29.	33	Royal Bank of Scotland Group	79.	65	McDonald's Restaurants
30.	39	Lloyds Banking Group	80.	NEW	Centrica
31.	22	Microsoft	81.	91	EDF Energy
32.	49	Sainsbury's	82.	74	Bain & Company
33.	60	MI5 – The Security Service	83.	47	Cadbury (now part of Kraft Foods)
34.	27	Police	84.	63	DLA Piper
35.	50	Royal Navy	85.	68	BDO
36.	36	BAE Systems	86.	93	Nestlé
37.	26	Clifford Chance	87.	NEW	Jaguar Land Rover
38.	46	Cancer Research UK	88.	81	E.ON
39.	41	Slaughter and May	89.	84	QinetiQ
40.	51	Morgan Stanley	90.	85	npower
41.	82	ASDA	91.	NEW	BNP Paribas
42.	38	McKinsey & Company	92.	NEW	Lloyd's
43.	53	Barclays Capital	93.	NEW	Sony
44.	59	UBS	94.	79	Penguin
45.	58	Sky	95.	NEW	Diageo
46.	34	Arup	96.	56	GCHQ
47.	29	Local Government	97.	NEW	Baker & McKenzie
48.	31	Mars	98.	NEW	Vodafone
49.	NEW	Saatchi & Saatchi	99.	100	Siemens
50.	42	Linklaters	100.	NEW	Santander

Source **The UK Graduate Careers Survey 2010**, High Fliers Research Ltd. 16,114 final year students leaving UK universities in the summer of 2010 were asked 'Which employer do you think offers the best opportunities for graduates?'

or experiences through the recruitment and selection process. Finalists also considered the level of vacancies that organisations were recruiting for as an indicator of possible employment prospects, or were influenced by employers' profile on campus.

Many final year students, however, used the 'employment proposition' as their main guide – the quality of graduate training and development an employer offers, the salary & remuneration package available, and the practical aspects of a first job such as location or working hours.

Irrespective of the criteria that students used to arrive at their answer, the hardest part for many was just selecting a single organisation. To some extent, choosing two or three, or even half a dozen employers would have been much easier. But the whole purpose of the exercise was to replicate the reality that everyone faces – you can only work for one organisation. And at each stage of the job search there are choices to be made as to which direction to take and which employers to pursue.

The resulting *Top 100* is a dynamic league table of the UK's most exciting and well-respected graduate recruiters in 2010. For an unprecedented seventh consecutive year, the accounting and professional services firm PricewaterhouseCoopers has been voted the UK's leading graduate employer with a total of 9.1 per cent of finalists' votes. The firm has a lead of more than five hundred votes over rivals Deloitte who remain in second place for the fifth year running.

Despite polling slightly fewer votes than in 2009, the Civil Service has moved up into third place. KPMG has increased its share of the vote by a sixth and is now ranked in fourth place. Having doubled its vote last year and reached the top three employers, discount retailer Aldi has slipped back this year to 5th place. The NHS is unchanged in 6th position but the widely acclaimed Teach First scheme has climbed another place to 7th, continuing its unbroken seven-year rise up the rankings since entering the *Top 100* in 63rd place in 2003. Accenture drop back one place to 8th and both the BBC and Ernst & Young are unchanged in 9th and 10th places respectively.

Goldman Sachs has moved back up the rankings after losing half its vote in 2009 and is now in 15th place. Barclays Bank has more than doubled its share of the vote this year and has jumped an impressive eighteen places to reach 17th position. Tesco has climbed a further four places this year and L'Oréal has reached the top twenty for the first time, one of twenty-two employers to achieve their best-ever rankings in this year's *Top 100*.

A number of leading retailers have done well in this year's rankings. Marks & Spencer have moved up to 21st place and the John Lewis Partnership – which includes its department stores and the Waitrose supermarket chain – has jumped seventeen places to 28th place, the first time it has appeared in the top thirty. Sainsbury's has climbed seventeen places to 32nd place and Boots, the health and beauty retailer, has improved its position too, moving up fifteen places to 60th.

The City's disastrous year in the wake of the 'credit crunch', the collapse of Lehman Brothers and the resulting global financial meltdown had a dramatic impact on the rankings of banking and financial institutions in the 2009 edition of the *Top 100*. Twelve months on, the prospects for City recruiters seem brighter and twelve of the sixteen banking and financial institutions featured in the new rankings have improved their positions.

The highest climbers in this year's *Top 100* are led by Asda which has jumped an impressive forty-one places to 41st, Lidl which leaps thirty-five places to 54th and accountancy firm Grant Thornton which moves up thirty-one places to 68th in the *Top 100*. MI5 – the Security Service has also done very well, climbing from 93rd place in 2008 to 60th in 2009 and now 33rd in the latest rankings.

There are a total of eleven new entries or re-entries in this year's *Top 100*, the highest being Saatchi & Saatchi, the advertising agency which joins the rankings in 49th place, the strongest debut for a new employer since 2003. Engineering company Balfour Beatty, energy group Centrica and Lloyd's appear for the first time in 69th place, 80th place and 92nd place respectively.

Jaguar Land Rover, BNP Paribas, Sony, Diageo and Baker & McKenzie have each returned to the *Top 100* after dropping out of the list in previous years, as does Vodafone, the mobile phone company which last appeared in the rankings in 2004. Santander, the bank formed from the takeovers of Abbey, the Alliance & Leicester and part of the Bradford & Bingley bank is a new entry in 100th place.

Organisations leaving the *Top 100* in 2010 include beleaguered airline British Airways, steelmaker Corus, Apple, Innocent Drinks, HP, Norton Rose, the Financial Services Authority, the Defence Science & Technology Laboratory, the Environment Agency and Data Connection, which changed its name to Metaswitch Networks in 2009. HBOS is now included within the Lloyds Banking Group.

This year's edition of *The Times Top 100 Graduate Employers* has produced a number of significant changes within the rankings and the results provide a unique insight into how graduates from the 'Class of 2010' rated the UK's leading employers. Almost all of these organisations are featured in the 'Employer Entry' section of this book. From page 57, you can see a two-page profile for each employer, listed alphabetically for easy reference.

The editorial part of the entry includes a short description of what the organisation does, its opportunities for graduates and its recruitment programme for 2010-2011. A fact file for each employer gives details of the number of graduate vacancies, the business functions that graduates are recruited for, likely starting salaries for 2011,

application deadlines, the universities that the employer is intending to visit during the year, and contact details for their recruitment website and graduate brochure. The right-hand page of the entry contains a display advert for the employer.

If you would like to find out more about any of the employers featured in *The Times Top 100 Graduate Employers*, then you can use the book's 'Information Request Service' – simply register your personal details and the employers you are interested in using the request card that appears opposite page 248, or go online to **www.Top100GraduateEmployers.com** – the official website showcasing the latest news and information about *Top 100* organisations.

You'll receive regular email bulletins about the employers, details of their presentations and careers events at your university, and the latest news about the organisations. The service is entirely free and you choose which employers you would like to hear about.

Using the 'Information Request Service' enters you into a prize draw to win **£5,000** and the first **500** people to register with the service will receive a free copy of *The Graduate Jobs Formula* book. There are also fifty **£50 iTunes vouchers** to be won – one at each of the universities at which *The Times Top 100 Graduate Employers* book is distributed – for those who register before **30th November 2010**.

THE TIMES TOP 100 GRADUATE EMPLOYERS

Employers in this year's Top 100

		Number of Employers			Number of Employers
1.	Public Sector Employer	12	9.	Accountancy or Professional Services Firm	6
2.	Retailer	11	10.	IT or Telecoms Company	5
3.	Engineering or Industrial Company	10	11.	Media Company	5
4.	Investment Bank	10	12.	Consulting Firm	4
5.	Law Firm	9	13.	Armed Forces	3
6.	Consumer Goods Company	8	14.	Chemical or Pharmaceutical Company	2
7.	Oil or Energy Company	7	15.	Charity or Voluntary Sector	2
8.	Bank or Financial Institution	6			

Source **The UK Graduate Careers Survey 2010**, High Fliers Research Ltd. 16,114 final year students leaving UK universities in the summer 2010 were asked 'Which employer do you think offers the best opportunities for graduates?'

Being the one to inspire peer group envy

pwc

Helping create value through:

Assurance

Consulting

Tax

Financial Advisory

Actuarial

PwC Legal

You need a 2:1 or above in any degree discipline. From 300 UCAS tariff or equivalent.

We value diversity in our people

Build a CV others envy. Our graduate training gives you breadth as well as depth of knowledge. Learn from expert practitioners, earn professional qualifications, work with great clients and experience different roles to ensure you always stand out from the crowd.

We work with our clients to measure, protect and enhance what matters most to them. So if you're serious about a career in business we don't think anyone else could give you a better start. Students agree: we're proud they've voted us number one in *The Times Top 100 Graduate Employers* survey for the last seven years. To build real value into your CV contact us.

Visit pwc.com/uk/careers. Text 'pwc' to 85792 to find your nearest PwC event.*

© 2010 PricewaterhouseCoopers LLP. All rights reserved. "PwC" refers to PricewaterhouseCoopers LLP (the limited liability partnership registered in the United Kingdom), PricewaterhouseCoopers Legal LLP ("PwC Legal", the limited liability partnership registered in the United Kingdom) or, as the context requires, the PricewaterhouseCoopers global network or other member firms of the network, each of which is a separate legal entity.
*Texts charged at your standard network rate.

The Times Graduate Recruitment Awards

As well as *The Times Top 100 Graduate Employers* league table, students from the 'Class of 2010' were also asked 'Which employer would you most like to work for?' to identify the 'graduate employers of choice' for different career destinations. The winners of *The Times Graduate Recruitment Awards 2010* are listed here:

Source **The UK Graduate Careers Survey 2010**, High Fliers Research Ltd. 16,114 final year students leaving university in the summer 2010 were asked 'Which employer do you most want to work for?' within the career sectors they had applied to.

The difference isn't just in the engine, it's in the engineer.

Engineering · Finance · Supply Chain · Purchasing · Manufacturing Leadership · HR · Commercial · Customer Management · Project Management

Graduate Opportunities

With 16 per cent better fuel efficiency than the first Trent aero engine, the new Trent XWB you see here has been designed for low emissions and improved environmental performance. Now take a look at the person standing next to it. Mike joined our graduate programme in 2009 and is one of a 39,000-strong global team who make groundbreaking feats of innovation like this possible. See the difference we can make to your career.

Trusted to deliver excellence

www.rolls-royce.com/careers

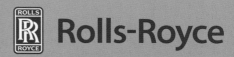

Rolls-Royce

How to use the directory

Many of the employers listed within The Times Top 100 Graduate Employers are featured in the 'Employer Entries' section of the directory. These entries describe what each organisation does, the opportunities they offer graduates, and practical details about their recruitment programme for 2010-2011.

The 'Employer Entry' section begins on page 57.

Each entry follows a standard format, and contains two elements: descriptive text and easy-to-find information on the employer's vacancies, contact details and salary expectations.

Locations of jobs
The regional locations of the employer's jobs are highlighted in red.

Vacancies
The number of likely graduate vacancies at this employer in 2010-2011

Employer's graduate recruitment website

Career areas recruited for
Details of the generic career areas that the employer recruits into. There are 17 areas to look out for:

- Accountancy
- Consulting
- Engineering
- Finance
- General Management
- Human Resources
- Investment Banking
- IT
- Law
- Logistics
- Manufacturing
- Marketing
- Media
- Purchasing
- Research & Development
- Retailing
- Sales

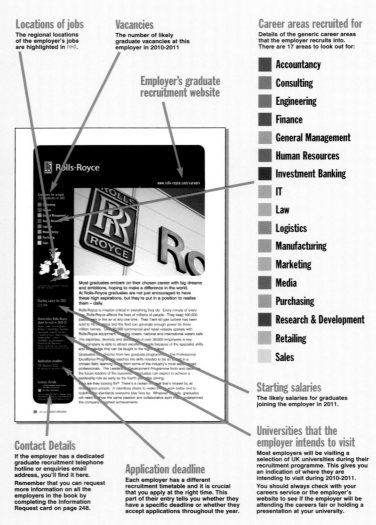

Starting salaries
The likely salaries for graduates joining the employer in 2011.

Universities that the employer intends to visit
Most employers will be visiting a selection of UK universities during their recruitment programme. This gives you an indication of where they are intending to visit during 2010-2011. You should always check with your careers service or the employer's website to see if the employer will be attending the careers fair or holding a presentation at your university.

Contact Details
If the employer has a dedicated graduate recruitment telephone hotline or enquiries email address, you'll find it here. Remember that you can request more information on all the employers in the book by completing the Information Request card on page 248.

Application deadline
Each employer has a different recruitment timetable and it is crucial that you apply at the right time. This part of their entry tells you whether they have a specific deadline or whether they accept applications throughout the year.

The official engineering design services provider for the London 2012 Games

Aim higher

Join our Graduate Development Programme and together we'll build a brighter future for everyone.

Instead of leading you down a set career path, we'll open doors by giving you choices about how your career unfolds and providing a breadth of projects to gain experience on. And as one of the leading infrastructure consultancies, we're well placed to invest in your development and offer the career opportunities you're looking for.

If you share our boundless curiosity and drive to improve the world in which we all live, work and play, it's a chance to become an expert in whatever inspires you most.

Make the story of your career a more interesting one. To find out more and apply, visit **www.atkinsglobal.com/graduates/times**

Aerospace
Building Design
Communication & Systems
Conventional Power
Defence
Environment
Finance
Geotechnics & Tunnelling
Highways
Intelligent Transport Systems
Management Consultancy
Nuclear Power
Oil & Gas
Rail & Metro
Transport Planning
Water

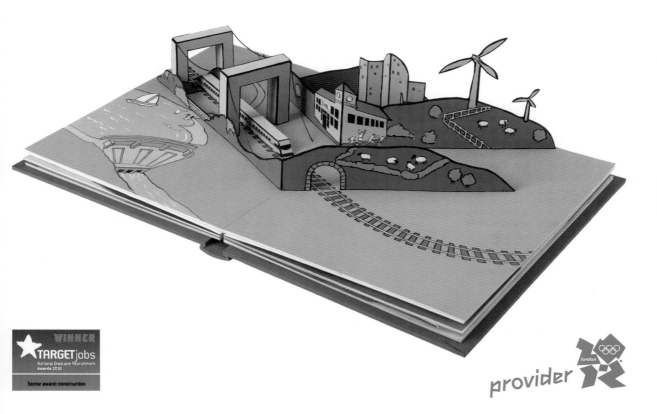

provider

Plan Design Enable

© Atkins Ltd except where stated otherwise. The Atkins logo, the "open A" device and the strapline "Plan Design Enable" are trademarks of Atkins Ltd. The official Emblem of the London Organising Committee of the Olympic Games and Paralympic Games Ltd is © 2007 The London Organising Committee of the Olympic Games and Paralympic Games Limited. All rights reserved.

"There I was… keys in hand about to open the store, *my* store, on my first day. It felt fantastic."

Brand, Buying & Marketing | Retail Management | Finance | IT

"I joined Boots' graduate programme two years ago and now I manage a local store. The moment I arrived at the store on my first day was incredible. I stood there and thought, 'This is huge' – I had such a sense of achievement and ownership. The programme was really intense but I had great support and training. I learned something new every day. Now it was time to put it all into practice."

We offer real jobs with real responsibility. After all, our graduate programme is about creating leaders of the future – people who will be the heart of our business. Whichever programme you choose, you'll cover much more than your own specific area. We'll support you with structured training that touches on every aspect of Boots, so you quickly gain a rounded view of the commercial realities of how we work. And if you demonstrate a real desire and passion to succeed, you'll have the opportunity to fast-track your career through our business.

Read Emma's full story, and discover many more like it, at

www.boots.jobs/graduates

THE SUNDAY TIMES
25
BEST BIG
COMPANIES
TO WORK FOR
2010

feel good

Emma, **Store Manager**

Class of 2009 will take this year's job offers

"But students leaving university this summer will be disappointed to find new positions have ... graduates from

where vacancies in investment banking have risen by a third. The number of job opportunities in high street banks, accounting and professional services ... cent rise this year ... ent drop in 20

Graduate jobs on the rise afte two-year slump

GR DUATE vacanci

Graduates fight for jobs in competitive market

GRADUATES str...

Students 'still face fight to land job'

University leav... face stiff compet... graduate jobs this... despite a rise in th... of vacancies, r... gests today.

While empl... take on 17.9 p... graduates this... year, there ar... cants on a...

seek any ...upation to ...dence and ... skills base, ...ard, AGR ...ve.

...prospects ...y bleak. In... ...rket re... ...High ...to... pub... ...week ...16,000 ...s, with ...17.9 ...duate ...itive ...con... ...ne. ...m-

a seven per in applicatio... Certain sector competitive, graduates chas... media job, and ...plicants trying ...tions at Unil... Proctor and Gan... to lucrati... salaries in ... goods ind...

Results fr... High Fliers ... subject of g... ing salaries ... they have b... £25,000 for ... years, wh... Fliers show... £29,00...

The chances of landing a graduate job? One in 270

consumer goods firms such as Unilever and Procter and Gamble, which offer relatively few jobs but lucrative starting salaries each 270.2 applicants chasing each vacancy.

The study, by High Fliers ... looked at the 100 firms

the public sector was unique among industries in increasing recruitment, taking on 4.6 per cent more graduates.

The study concluded that the continuing expansion of higher education was also behind the intense rivalry for jobs at leading firms. Universities turned out 50,000 mo... graduates this summer than m... left London

August to concentrate on her ... of landing a research role ... more voluntary work lined u... She is also considering tra... to Canada to study for a ... degree after finding the cost... UK extortionate.

"Many of my friends work... and shops, alongside peop... didn't go to university. ... "It's really difficult for all o... can't do what we want to d... Martin Birchall, director... Research, said: "Un...

Testing time is ove for graduate marke

BY SYMON ROSS

A NEW update on the graduate job market has confirmed that after two years of swingeing cuts in graduate recruitment, vacancies for those leaving university this summer have increased substantially.

Howeve... the UK-wide by H...

competition to land a good graduate job this summer. Employers have already received an unprecedented number of applications this year for their graduate vacancies and many organisations have now filled all their places for 2010 or have clo...

On the downside recruiters said that this year they were getting on average 45 applications for every vacancy, a rise of 7% on last year and up 15% on 200...

The...

Competition... est for graduat... goods manuf... firm... b... er

Increase expected in graduate jobs

Vacancies for graduates are set to rise by 11.8 per cent this year after two years of substantial cuts, according to a survey of the 100 leading grad... employers. Bu... by Hi...

There's good news, and there's bad new

More entry-level positions of... new gradua... competition... tougher, rep... Martin Bir...

Graduates in the workplace

Students face up to bleak futures

By Aidan Radnedge

...over salaries and even ... ...thousands ...

...ue students were prepar... ...cept low-paid work in ... supermarkets and call ... according to analysts ... igh Flie... Re...

chall of High Fliers Research, which commissioned the study.

Expectations have dropped – but students still expect to earn an average £22,000 for their first job.

...usiness and IT stu... ...saying salarie...

More top jobs oper up for graduates

Each vacancy sees 45 applications

Some of larg...

and professional service... firms.

Graduate salaries have increased significantly over

Graduates in scramble for top jobs

UNIVERSITY leavers face a jobs scramble as 45 chase every vacant post for high ... a poll has found.

... ...uate

Student fears over jobs

By Graeme Paton

ONLY a quarter of arts and ...umanities final-year students ...pect to start graduate jobs ...s summer, according to a ...dy published yesterday.

...housands of final-year

on a "substantial backlog" in the number of jobless graduates from previous years, which is creating additional pressure in the employment market in 2010.

Martin Birchall, from High Fliers Research, said: "Students from arts and humanities courses and those who've had little or no... xperi...

Students face fight with last year's graduates for job

Starting salaries frozen for successful applicants

Joanna Sugden

...tudents applying for graduate jobs in ...eptember will find that a quarter of ...acancies have been filled by last year's ...aduates, according to a survey of ...ployers.

The record number of students finish... ...g university this summer mean ...petition for jobs as recruitment re... ...ins in the doldrums and ...

time, at an average of £27,000. They rose by 5.9 per cent in 2009 and by 4.9 per cent the year before but will not change in 2010.

The Graduate Market 2010 survey suggests that the 100 biggest graduate employers have increased their vacancies by 11.8 per cent this year compared with 2009. But cuts in recruitment in the past two years, a significant in...

unemployed people aged 16 to 25 has reached its highest level and the next round of employment statistics is expected to show that one million are out of work.

Of the 1,001 final-year students surveyed by High Fliers, 25 per cent said that they had applied for jobs that they

the Army, Teach First, a charity tha... cruits high-achieving graduates int... classroom, KPMG, the consultancy ... pany, and the Royal Air Force. Howe... the highest number of jobs for grad... that any of them can offer is 1,039.
● The deadline for degree applica...

Understanding the Graduate Market

by Martin Birchall
Managing Director, High Fliers Research

Bleak newspaper headlines screaming that Britain's most popular employers have received a record 270 applications per vacancy in 2010 did little to reassure this year's university-leavers that the worst of the recent slump in graduate recruitment is now over.

There were fears too that many of 2010's best vacancies would be snapped up by the tens of thousands of graduates from the 'Class of 2009' who failed to find work last year. For many job hunters, it seemed like the employment prospects for graduates were worse than ever.

But in reality, entry-level vacancies at the organisations featured in *The Times Top 100 Graduate Employers* did rise sharply in 2010. With the recession in the UK officially over, many leading employers opted to step up their recruitment and the number of graduate jobs available increased by almost a fifth. This was the first annual rise in vacancies for three years – graduate vacancies were cut by a quarter during the 2008 and 2009 recruitment seasons.

The outlook for the 'Class of 2011' is brighter too – vacancies at *The Times Top 100 Graduate Employers* are set to increase by a further 6.8 per cent in 2011. Two-fifths of employers in the *Top 100* plan to hire more graduates this recruitment season than in 2010, a third believe they will recruit similar numbers, while a quarter expect to reduce their total graduate intake. Together, the employers in this year's *Top 100*

are advertising 17,862 jobs, compared to the 16,727 graduates hired in 2010.

The banking sector was one of the employment areas hardest hit at the beginning of the recession but it has been amongst the first to show signs of real recovery. City investment banks increased their graduate recruitment by almost 40 per cent in 2010 and are set to expand their vacancies by another third in 2011, restoring almost all the entry-level positions that were cut during 2008 and 2009.

Other sectors are optimistic too. The leading retailers, IT & telecommunications firms and consumer goods manufacturers are planning to recruit up to a third more graduates in the coming year. There are smaller increases in vacancies at the top legal firms, management consultants and at accountancy and professional services firms.

Vacancy numbers are unchanged for the Armed Forces, in the charity & voluntary sector and at media organisations. But there are expected to be a few less graduate jobs available at the oil & energy companies, chemical & pharmaceuticals firms, engineering & industrial employers and at the high street banks. There is also considerable uncertainty about graduate posts in the public sector, with fewer entry-level positions predicted for 2011.

There are now an average of 175 vacancies per *Top 100* employer but one in eight organisations plan to hire at least 250 new recruits and two

It's not where you started,
it's where you're going that matters.
Just another day at the office
for a high performer.

Choose Accenture for a career where the variety of opportunities and challenges allows you to make a difference every day. A place where you can develop your potential and grow professionally, working alongside talented colleagues. The only place where you can learn from our unrivalled experience, while helping our global clients achieve high performance.

If this is your idea of a typical working day, then Accenture is the place to be.

Visit accenture.com/top100
• Consulting • Technology • Outsourcing

accenture
High performance. Delivered.

© 2010 Accenture. All rights reserved.

employers anticipate hiring at least 1,000 university-leavers in 2010.

The largest number of vacancies in 2011 are at accountancy firms (22.4 per cent of total graduate jobs), investment banks and fund managers (18.5 per cent of total) and the public sector employers (10.6 per cent of total). Together the 'Big Four' accountancy firms – PricewaterhouseCoopers, Deloitte, KPMG and Ernst & Young – plan to recruit more than 3,500 graduate trainees. The public sector remains well-represented in this year's *Top 100*, with twelve Government departments and agencies appearing in the latest league table.

Employers planning to recruit the fewest new graduates in 2011 include those in the chemical & pharmaceutical sector (0.4 per cent of total graduate jobs), charities (1.1 per cent) and consumer goods manufacturers (2.0 per cent).

The biggest individual recruiters in *The Times Top 100 Graduate Employers* during 2010-2011 are PricewaterhouseCoopers and Deloitte (1,000 vacancies each), KPMG (650 vacancies), the Army (750 vacancies), the recently-expanded Teach First scheme (730 places), Ernst & Young (650 vacancies) and the Royal Bank of Scotland Group, UBS and the Civil Service Fast Stream (each 500 vacancies). The smallest recruiters are

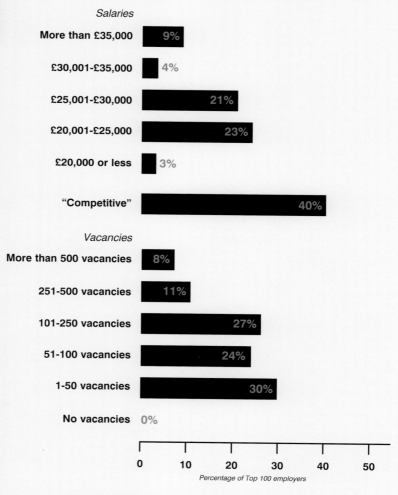

THE TIMES TOP 100 GRADUATE EMPLOYERS

Graduate Salaries & Vacancies in 2011

Salaries

More than £35,000	9%
£30,001-£35,000	4%
£25,001-£30,000	21%
£20,001-£25,000	23%
£20,000 or less	3%
"Competitive"	40%

Vacancies

More than 500 vacancies	8%
251-500 vacancies	11%
101-250 vacancies	27%
51-100 vacancies	24%
1-50 vacancies	30%
No vacancies	0%

0   10   20   30   40   50

Percentage of Top 100 employers

Source **The Times Top 100 Graduate Employers 2010-11**, High Fliers Research Ltd. Graduate starting salaries & vacancy levels in 2011, compared with recruitment in 2010 at the organisations featured in The Times Top 100 Graduate Employers

Agility

Your unique talents and hard work make success look easy.

Face challenges with confidence. Nimbly navigate every obstacle in your path. It's that unique quality that's positioned you where you are today. And it's what we value at Bank of America. Join our team, and we'll open your career path and give you new opportunities to take the possible and make it real. We'll solicit your input and provide training, mentorship, and support to boost your aspirations to a global level. And as part of the world's leading financial institution, you can create the kind of opportunity that begets greater opportunity and bigger impact than you ever imagined.

Set opportunity in motion.

bankofamerica.com/campusrecruiting

© 2010 Bank of America Corporation. All rights reserved.

Bank of America
Merrill Lynch

Saatchi & Saatchi, Cadbury (now part of Kraft Foods) and WPP, which each plan to hire fewer than 15 graduates for their organisations in 2011.

Looking at the roles on offer from *Top 100* employers, more than two thirds have vacancies for graduates in financial management and at least half are recruiting IT staff. At least a third have opportunities in engineering, human resources and marketing, a quarter are looking for sales executives or have roles in purchasing, whilst a fifth are looking for retail personnel.

Research from *The UK Graduate Careers Survey 2010* – a survey of more than 16,000 final year students from the 'Class of 2010' conducted by High Fliers Research – showed that almost

half of new graduates wanted to work in London for their first job. It's good news then that more than three-quarters of *Top 100* employers have graduate vacancies in the capital and half have posts available elsewhere in the south east of England. Half also have vacancies in Yorkshire, the Midlands, the south west and north west of England and in Scotland. Fewer than two-fifths of organisations have opportunities in Wales or Northern Ireland. The region with the fewest graduate employers is East Anglia.

Although graduate starting salaries at Britain's leading employers continued rising during the recession, more than four-fifths of the organisations in this year's edition of *The Times*

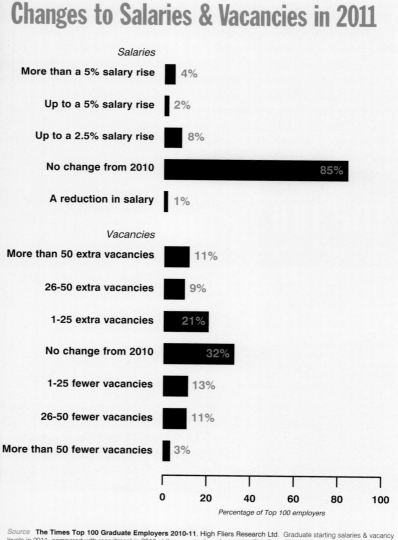

Changes to Salaries & Vacancies in 2011

Salaries

More than a 5% salary rise	4%
Up to a 5% salary rise	2%
Up to a 2.5% salary rise	8%
No change from 2010	85%
A reduction in salary	1%

Vacancies

More than 50 extra vacancies	11%
26-50 extra vacancies	9%
1-25 extra vacancies	21%
No change from 2010	32%
1-25 fewer vacancies	13%
26-50 fewer vacancies	11%
More than 50 fewer vacancies	3%

Percentage of Top 100 employers

Source **The Times Top 100 Graduate Employers 2010-11**, High Fliers Research Ltd. Graduate starting salaries & vacancy levels in 2011, compared with recruitment in 2010 at the organisations featured in The Times Top 100 Graduate Employers

Top 100 Graduate Employers have opted to leave their starting salaries unchanged from 2010 rates. Only a sixth of employers have announced increases to their graduate packages for 2011, most by between two and four per cent. The average salary for graduates in 2010 was £29,000.

Almost half of Top 100 employers simply describe their salary packages for 2011 as "competitive". A quarter expect to offer new graduates up to £25,000 and nine organisations – typically either investment banks or City law firms – offer starting salaries in excess of £35,000. But the most generous graduate package publicised within this edition of the Top 100 is for retailer Aldi – they're providing their new recruits with a starting salary of £40,000 as well as a fully-expensed Audi A4 company car.

The majority of the organisations listed in The Times Top 100 Employers are actively marketing their graduate vacancies at between 15 and 20 UK universities this year. Recruiters use a variety of careers fairs, campus presentations, local advertising and promotions with the university careers services. The universities likely to host the most events run by Britain's top graduate employers in 2010-2011 are Cambridge, Warwick, Manchester, London, Oxford and Bristol.

Half of the UK's leading employers now recruit all the year round and will accept applications throughout the 2010-2011 recruitment season, until all their vacancies have been filled. For employers with a single application deadline, the majority are in either November or December, although most law firms usually have July closing dates.

Few people can expect to walk straight into a good graduate job – the employers listed in the Top 100 received an average of 45 applications per vacancy in 2010 and all have rigorous selection procedures which include online applications, initial interviews, aptitude tests and final-round assessment centres.

It's not only important to gain a good degree – most of the top employers now insist that applicants have either a First or 2.1 – but also develop key skills along the way. Employers look for well-rounded individuals with demonstrable competencies such as the ability to work well in teams, good organisational and communication skills, and strong leadership potential.

But for those finalists who do make the grade, there continue to be many rewarding careers and some great starting salaries on offer at The Times Top 100 Graduate Employers.

THE TIMES TOP 100 GRADUATE EMPLOYERS

Graduate Employment in 2011, by Industry

2010			% of total vacancies in 2011	How graduate vacancies compare with 2010
1.	1	Accountancy or Professional Services Firms	22.4	Up 1.0%
2.	4	Investment Banks or Fund Managers	18.5	Up 33.7%
3.	2	Public Sector	10.6	Down 4.6%
4.	3	Armed Forces	10.1	No change
5.	5	Banking or Financial Services	6.7	Down 1.0%
6.	6	Retailers	6.2	Up 15.9%
7.	7	Engineering or Industrial Companies	4.6	Down 1.0%
8.	8	Law Firms	4.6	Up 7.8%
9.	10	Consulting Firms	3.1	Up 2.8%
10.	12	Media Organisations	3.1	No change
11.	9	Oil & Energy Companies	2.7	Down 5.7%
12.	11	IT & Telecommunications Companies	2.5	Up 21.3%
13.	14	Consumer Goods Manufacturers	2.0	Up 34.7%
14.	13	Charity or Voluntary Organisations	1.1	No change
15.	15	Chemical & Pharmaceuticals	0.4	Down 3.0%

Source **The Times Top 100 Graduate Employers 2010-11**, High Fliers Research Ltd. Graduate vacancy levels in 2011, compared with total numbers recruited in 2010 at the organisations featured in The Times Top 100 Graduate Employers

CALLING ALL OF NATURE'S GREAT PERFORMERS.

The dolphin. The ultimate listening device. Inspired by a dolphin's sonar, our Astute submarine sonar system has the world's largest number of hydrophones, giving it the biggest ears of any sonar system in service today. In fact, the perfect performance in nature is a great source of inspiration for our people, who are always looking to develop the most effective defence, aerospace and security systems on earth.

BUSINESS | **ENGINEERING** | **FINANCE**

baesystems.com/graduates

BAE SYSTEMS

REAL PERFORMANCE. REAL ADVANTAGE.

Anything
but ordinary

Quality products. Quality people.

There's nothing ordinary about our Graduate opportunities…

OR OUR GRADUATES!

Graduate Area Management Programme
LOCATIONS NATIONWIDE

Are you anything but ordinary?

If you can lead and inspire as part of a team, take the next step now towards running multiple stores with a world-class retailer.

Our fast-track Area Management programme is for outstanding and self-confident graduates who will make a significant difference to our business from day one. There is a steep learning curve and we'll give you the chance to take early responsibility of a district of up to five stores.

Your application should reflect your high standards and attention to detail.

For more information please visit **www.lidl.co.uk**

NATIONAL COUNCIL FOR WORK EXPERIENCE
AWARDS FINALIST 2009/10

www.lidl.co.uk

Successful Job Hunting

by Catherine Richardson
Head of Careers Advisory Service, Durham University

The sooner you start preparing for your future, the more likely you are to be successful if you're looking for a graduate job after university. Ever-earlier application deadlines, increased competition for places and a growing emphasis on work experience means that many more students now look into their employment options in their first year.

There are thousands of finalists each year who miss opportunities because they've started the job hunting process too late. And even those who begin their careers research in their penultimate year may find it difficult to fit in an internship – that long summer holiday before the final year doesn't exist for students who have dissertations to finish.

Help is at hand, though, because every university in the UK has its own dedicated careers service that can provide a wealth of information and guidance, irrespective of your career aspirations or your year of study. Plenty of undergraduates say how daunting it is to make that initial step and come into the careers service. It's all too easy to make excuses about 'I've got too much on' or 'I've got to get my good degree' but when students do visit for the first time, many often say 'I wish I'd started earlier'.

People often worry about saying 'I haven't got a clue' or 'I don't know what I want to do' but actually those are the most common enquiries at careers services. It isn't a problem – that is what we do and what we're here to help with. You don't have to have an idea.

When you do come into your university careers service, there are a number of resources that may be a useful starting point. The first person you'll meet at a careers service isn't likely to be a receptionist – they are usually information professionals who are experienced at getting students started with their job search, and will help you familiarise yourself with the resources available and make the best use of the careers service.

Prospects Planner can be a good starting point. It's an online tool which matches your interests, strengths and abilities with specific job types and can be a very effective way to think through the type of jobs that you might want to do. The process encourages you to take a step back and examine 'what do I actually want?' – whether it's working regular hours, having a stable and secure role, or joining a good training programme. It can also be a good way to challenge your pre-conceptions about different jobs and the often misleading stereotypes associated with them.

You can also find out from alumni files what other students from your degree subject have gone into. This can be quite revealing because at least half of the vacancies advertised at careers services are not targeted at a specific degree discipline.

REVEALED!

The **secret formula** to winning a **graduate job**

Find out how to land your **dream career** and...

Maximise your **employability**...

Stand out from other graduates...

Multiply your chances of **getting a job**...

The Graduate Jobs Formula

HOW TO LAND YOUR DREAM CAREER

PAUL REDMOND

$E = Q + WE + S \times C$

Employability = Qualifications + Work Experience + Strategies + Contacts

20% OFF

Estd. 1969 trotman **t**

GET 20% OFF YOUR COPY

Visit www.trotman.co.uk today and apply GRADHF at the checkout

One of the most important resources that university careers services offer is one-to-one guidance with a professional careers adviser. Particularly over the last two years, there has been a real growth in the number of students wanting to talk through what they could do after graduation, so advisers are in keen demand. At most universities, they are available through drop-in sessions – for quick queries such as CV advice or application guidance – as well as longer pre-booked appointments.

It is crucial to understand that an adviser isn't going to say 'you should be ...' or 'you should do ...', but will discuss with you what you've enjoyed doing at university, what your interests are and which skills you've developed. From there they can help you develop a plan of action for your job search. Careers advisers have a wide variety of backgrounds and many worked in industry or business before joining the careers service and have extensive experience of different aspects of the employment world.

It's unlikely you'll walk out the door after your first appointment with a careers adviser saying 'yes, I know exactly what I'm going to do now' – that's not an adviser's job – but they will help you understand more about the job hunting process and the timescales involved. For example, if you want to work in some of the most competitive areas, such as investment banking or management consultancy, then it's important to realise that application deadlines for many of these graduate schemes are right at the start of the final year.

At many careers services, their online resources have been growing rapidly, with much more emphasis on providing round-the-clock access to careers information and a corresponding move away from providing paper-based information. Generally, most services have not tried to replicate a whole careers library on their website but instead provide a guide to what type of help is available elsewhere online through directional links.

There are two key areas on careers service websites that can be especially useful – the latest graduate vacancies and details of local careers events that employers are holding at your university. The majority of careers services work with a wide range of national and international employers, as well as those from the local region,

so the website can provide up-to-the-minute details of the openings available. At Durham we have over 3,000 employers on our database who regularly recruit graduates and around a third of these are smaller or medium-sized local companies.

Once you've reflected on the type of work that you're interested in and the areas that match your skills and achievements, the challenge of researching what is available at individual employers begins. It's easy to assume that the main employment information about organisations will be on the graduate pages of their website. But often this will only explain the areas they're recruiting for, how they select and which competencies they're looking for. This is a useful starting point if you're trying to decide whether there's a match between your interests and experiences and their jobs, but it's very important to dig deeper and find out what other information your careers service has about the organisation.

They may well have reports from recent graduates describing their first experiences with the employer, the support they've had, the skills they've used and an impression of the culture of the organisation. Don't underestimate how much time this fact-finding process will take – any employer that you apply to will expect you to be able to say, in detail, why you want to work for them. Without having done the preparation, it's a very difficult question to answer.

When you are deliberating which employers to apply to for a graduate position, it can be easier to think of your first job after university as being just a next step, rather than a decision for the rest of your life. But remember, everyone's circumstances are different, so there is no single 'correct' strategy. For some people it's important to get good training and grounding with a large employer, others are more drawn to smaller organisations. Some students are keen to work in a particular location or feel they need to earn a certain amount in order to pay off their debts.

One of the best ways to find out about what an employer is really offering is to meet with them in person, either at a local careers fair or at one of their campus presentations. The fairs usually take place quite early in the autumn and to take full advantage of them, try and get as much preliminary research done as you can and

Administrative, Box-ticking, Bland?

It's time you looked at Human Resources from a different angle. Today's HR careers provide a pivotal role in international business, opening up a world of personal and professional opportunities. So with a career in HR the only boxes you'll tick are the ambitions you've fulfilled.

Vents at Paternoster Square, designed by Heatherwick Studio

Matthew Parker,
Assistant Manager,
Graduate Recruitment,
KPMG LLP

Matt is living proof there's more to HR than meets the eye. He's carved out an impressive career in global business at Tesco and KPMG, polishing up valuable skills in talent management, strategy and marketing along the way.

Think HR. Think again.
cipd.co.uk/thinkhr

prepare key questions you might want to ask employers beforehand. Careers fairs are not recruitment events as such, they're information fairs, so employers don't collect CVs or assess the students they meet. But nevertheless, it can be quite daunting to go and talk to recruiters on their stands.

As well as the major fairs, there are also events focusing on specific career sectors like science and engineering, finance or IT. In addition, many careers services run smaller less formal events on individual job types with recent alumni and local practitioners.

Many of the largest employers hold their own presentations at universities, during which they will 'sell' the opportunities at their organisation. Employers often try to bring recent graduates from that particular university to their event, so there's usually a good selection of people to answer your questions.

Between October and December, there are over a hundred presentations at the busiest universities. Careers services usually try to coordinate the events so that there aren't too many employers from the same sector on the same night.

If you can't go to a particular company that you're interested in, it might be worth going along to one held by a similar kind of organisation to find out more about the sector and the opportunities available.

We hear from a lot of students that their decision about which employers to apply to is often taken based on the people that they've met at the presentation – particularly when several employers within a sector are offering a similar training programme and salary package. As a result, employers often spend a great deal of time deciding which representatives to send to presentations because they know how important it is to make the right impression. Potential applicants will be asking 'can I see myself working with these people?'.

Before you launch into making your job applications, it is well worth compiling a CV that you can use as a reference, even though most of the best-known employers will insist that you complete their own on-line application forms. Preparing your CV is a very good way to draw together your experiences and record examples of the things that you've done at university that employers may be interested in such as teamwork, leadership or initiative. Most careers services run regular workshops on how to put

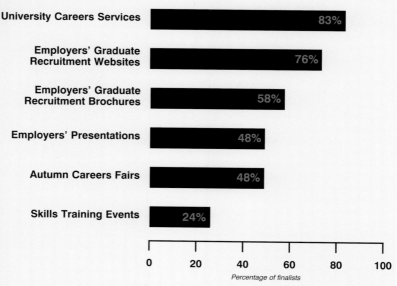

Recruitment Promotions used in 2009-10

Promotion	Percentage
University Careers Services	83%
Employers' Graduate Recruitment Websites	76%
Employers' Graduate Recruitment Brochures	58%
Employers' Presentations	48%
Autumn Careers Fairs	48%
Skills Training Events	24%

Percentage of finalists

Source **The UK Graduate Careers Survey 2010**, High Fliers Research Ltd. 16,114 final year students who left university in the summer of 2010 were asked about the recruitment promotions that they'd used or taken part in during 2009-2010.

together a CV and would encourage you to have a go at a draft before bringing it in for feedback from a careers adviser.

There isn't a 'right' amount of applications to make, but you have to be prepared to take time compiling each one individually. Employers often talk about receiving applications from students that have another employer's name in the text because applicants have copied and pasted information between different applications. It's a very easy mistake to make. It's equally important that if you're sending a copy of your CV to an employer to get your covering note right. You'll need to demonstrate that you know why you're interested in that employer, not just why you want a certain role. If you've done your homework and researched the employer, you should be able to answer that without just copying down something off their recruitment website.

If you're looking for a career in something like advertising, you will probably need to make many more applications than someone wanting to work in say finance or business. That's where the advice and guidance from your careers service can help you. It's also a good idea to spread your applications across different types of employers – not just the well-known names – there are some really good opportunities with smaller or medium-sized employers where you can get very similar experience.

Students often say that it takes them between ten and twelve hours to complete their first application, including the time needed to research the employer properly. After that it does become quicker because some of the preparation can be used again but it remains a very time-consuming process.

If your initial application is successful, the next stage in the selection process is usually an interview. Your careers service will be able to offer assistance in preparing for these – DVDs in the information room can give you a short introduction to what first-round interviews may include and careers advisers will be able to go through typical questions with you in a mock interview or group workshop.

The questions you'll face at interview are likely to be based around the application or CV but will

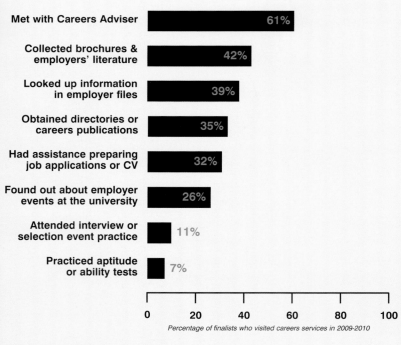

THE TIMES

TOP 100
GRADUATE EMPLOYERS

Careers Service Facilities used in 2009-10

Met with Careers Adviser	61%
Collected brochures & employers' literature	42%
Looked up information in employer files	39%
Obtained directories or careers publications	35%
Had assistance preparing job applications or CV	32%
Found out about employer events at the university	26%
Attended interview or selection event practice	11%
Practiced aptitude or ability tests	7%

0   20   40   60   80   100

Percentage of finalists who visited careers services in 2009-2010

Source **The UK Graduate Careers Survey 2010**, High Fliers Research Ltd. 16,114 final year students who left university in the summer of 2010 were asked about the facilities that they'd used at their local university careers service during 2009-2010.

With the ACA the whole world's calling.

THE ACA. QUALIFIED TO SUCCEED.

At home or abroad, the ACA opens up a world of career opportunities.

The ACA is a business and finance qualification from the ICAEW, a world leader of the accountancy and finance profession and is highly respected in all industry sectors around the world.

With an ACA you'll be able to work in any business, accountancy practice, not-for-profit organisation and the public sector – your career choices are endless.

If you're looking for variety, opportunity, and the best preparation for a career as a business leader, choose the ACA.

You'll be guaranteed a great reception anywhere in the world.

To find out more:
T +44 (0)1908 248 040
icaew.com/careers

also examine why you want that particular job, in that organisation. It's essential you get the practical aspects of an interview right – find out beforehand where you're going, make sure you arrive in good time and dress appropriately. Some employers still do their first interviews on campus but for most you will have to travel, either to a regional office or sometimes to their national headquarters.

Some interviews may be conducted by telephone and this can be harder because you don't get the eye contact or the face-to-face interaction. But you can at least have your notes or a copy of your application in front of you in front of you during the interview.

The final recruitment round is often a one or two-day selection centre. The style and content of these can vary enormously and could include several different activities, in addition to further one-to-one interviews. If you've been invited to a final-round selection day, try and find out beforehand from the company itself or from notes at the careers service what it might involve. Many careers services offer trial assessment centres for

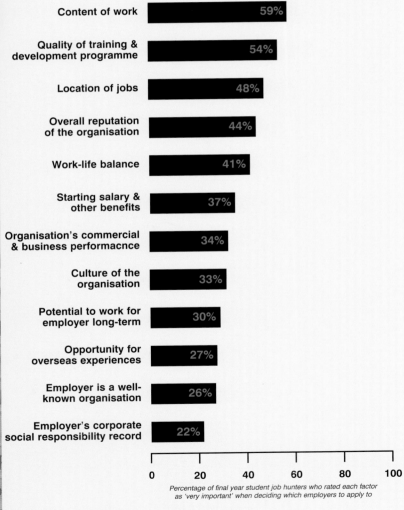

How Graduates Compared Employers in 2010

THE TIMES
TOP 100
GRADUATE EMPLOYERS

Factor	Percentage
Content of work	59%
Quality of training & development programme	54%
Location of jobs	48%
Overall reputation of the organisation	44%
Work-life balance	41%
Starting salary & other benefits	37%
Organisation's commercial & business performacnce	34%
Culture of the organisation	33%
Potential to work for employer long-term	30%
Opportunity for overseas experiences	27%
Employer is a well-known organisation	26%
Employer's corporate social responsibility record	22%

0   20   40   60   80   100

Percentage of final year student job hunters who rated each factor as 'very important' when deciding which employers to apply to

Source **The UK Graduate Careers Survey 2010**, High Fliers Research Ltd. 16,114 final year students who left university in the summer of 2010 were asked about their priorities when making applications to graduate employers in 2009-2010.

NetworkRail

Create a better future

Every day. Everywhere. We're doing this.

Over the next 10 years, Britain's rail traffic will increase by 30% – making ours the fastest-growing railway in Europe.

The work we carry out today will shape the Britain of tomorrow. By increasing capacity and encouraging innovation, we're creating improvements that will mean more trains, more services and better journeys for everyone. Our work will help Britain reach ambitious carbon emissions targets; it will power the economy.

We offer a range of multi-disciplinary programmes: from finance to engineering, management to IT. Build real experience through varied placements. Have a huge impact on diverse projects, and feel the pride you get from helping to develop the railways of tomorrow.

For more information, please visit networkrailgraduates.co.uk

candidates and can offer advice on how to handle group tasks or in-tray exercises.

By practicing aptitude tests, for example, you can improve your scores and it can take the element of fear out of the unexpected. Employers also run their own skills training workshops during the year to help job hunters understand the processes they use and what they are looking for during assessment centres. This last stage of recruitment is also a great way to see more of the employer and its culture – you may have the chance to visit the company's offices and meet with recent graduates and others who've been working there for a while.

At the end of your job hunting, if you're fortunate to get more than one job offer, your final challenge will be to decide which role to accept. The timing of job offers can be quite a problem. There may well be a lot going on with coursework or other academic commitments. Or you may have other interviews still in the pipeline. Take time to make your final decision and talk the situation through with your careers adviser.

Be aware that it is possible to go back to an employer and see if they are prepared to wait for an answer, perhaps until your other interviews are out of the way. It's not in an employer's best interests to have somebody accept an offer and then change their mind a few weeks down the line. But remember, once you've signed a contract, it is legally binding, so you need to be sure about your decision.

By the time you graduate, if you're in the difficult situation of not having had a job offer, then all is not lost. Not every employer recruits months in advance of their start dates and there are always a substantial number of one-off vacancies advertised through the university careers services over the summer months. And even once you've left university, you can continue to receive vacancy lists, email support and advice by telephone from your careers service. You can also use careers services at universities close to where you are living.

If you're considering doing a postgraduate course instead of continuing to look for employment, it's important that you're not simply doing it as a back-up plan. We would always ask someone who's considering further study what their drive was – it could be a love of the subject, it might be a vocational course or it could be that its about getting that extra something that an undergraduate degree doesn't provide.

Careers services can help you think through what your motivation is and how a postgraduate course might fit with your longer term career plans. It's a big decision to commit to a further year or two of study and a great deal of extra money too. The additional qualification won't come with a guarantee of a better chance in the graduate job market and for some, the best advice might be to try and get some extra work experience, rather than continue with additional studies.

THE TIMES
TOP 100
GRADUATE EMPLOYERS

Leading Destinations for 2010 Graduates

		% who wanted to work in sector			% who wanted to work in sector
1.	Media	15.2	11.	Sales	7.3
2.	Teaching	14.0	12.	Human Resources	6.5
3.	Marketing	13.9	13.	General Management	6.5
4.	Charity or Voluntary Work	11.3	14.	Retailing	5.7
5.	Consulting	10.6	15.	Finance	5.6
6.	Research & Development	10.3	16.	Buying or Purchasing	3.8
7.	Accountancy	10.3	17.	IT	3.5
8.	Investment Banking	10.1	18.	Armed Forces	3.4
9.	Law	9.5	19.	Police	2.9
10.	Engineering	7.6	20.	Property	2.3

Source **The UK Graduate Careers Survey 2010**, High Fliers Research Ltd. 16,114 final year students who left university in the summer of 2010 were asked which sectors they had applied to or planned to apply to for a graduate job.

INTELLIGENCE OFFICERS LONDON £24,750 + BENEFITS

Discretion is vital at MI5, the UK's security intelligence agency. Few people will know about the role you'll play in helping to safeguard national security. Every day you'll be making informed decisions that contribute towards MI5's efforts in countering terrorism, espionage, sabotage and the spread of weapons of mass destruction. Only you and your team will know you're protecting your community's way of life, and that's all that matters.

Whatever your degree, it's likely we have something that suits your skills and abilities. We are looking for highly capable, persuasive and analytical graduates with the confidence and resilience to handle a high level of responsibility early in your career. You will be supported by managers, peers and mentors and encouraged to expand your skill set through our careers academy, personal and professional courses and work experience in a range of our departments.

Do you have what it takes to be quietly successful? To find out more about the challenging, interesting and worthwhile careers we offer, visit **www.mi5.gov.uk/careers/graduates**

SECURITYSERVICE
MI5

Your future? Unsettled...

© 2010 Deloitte LLP. Deloitte LLP is an equal opportunities employer.

www.deloitte.co.uk/graduates

...or clear?

The possibilities are endless across our range of graduate and undergraduate opportunities in Audit, Tax, Consulting and Corporate Finance. If you're interested in joining a world-leading professional services firm that will challenge, develop and reward you in equal measure, visit www.deloitte.co.uk/graduates to see what's possible. It's your future. How far will you take it?

official professional services provider
to the Olympic and Paralympic Games

© 2010 Deloitte LLP. Deloitte LLP is an equal opportunities employer.

THE TIMES — TOP 100 GRADUATE EMPLOYERS — 2000-2001
THE TIMES — TOP 100 GRADUATE EMPLOYERS — 2001-2002
THE TIMES — TOP 100 GRADUATE EMPLOYERS — 2002-2003
THE TIMES — TOP 100 GRADUATE EMPLOYERS — 2003-2004
THE TIMES — TOP 100 GRADUATE EMPLOYERS — 2004-2005
THE TIMES — TOP 100 GRADUATE EMPLOYERS — 2005-2006
THE TIMES — TOP 100 GRADUATE EMPLOYERS — 2006-2007
THE TIMES — TOP 100 GRADUATE EMPLOYERS — 2007-2008
THE TIMES — TOP 100 GRADUATE EMPLOYERS — 2008-2009
THE TIMES — TOP 100 GRADUATE EMPLOYERS — 2009-2010

Ten Years of Researching Britain's Top Employers

by Gill Thomas
Publisher, The Times Top 100 Graduate Employers

Just as the first edition of *The Times Top 100 Graduate Employers* was being distributed to the 'Class of 2000' at the UK's leading universities, the Millenium Dome opened its doors for business, reality TV show *Big Brother* went on air for the first time, Ken Livingstone was elected Mayor of London, Great Britain won twenty-eight medals in the Sydney Olympics, the Royal Bank of Scotland took over Natwest Bank and children's character Bob the Builder had the unlikely best-selling single of the year with 'Can We Fix It?' .

For new graduates fresh out of university, the year 2000 wasn't a bad time to be job hunting. After a dip in recruitment the previous year, entry-level vacancies shot up by almost 15 per cent, one of the largest annual increases since the late 1980s and starting salaries continued to rise at nearly double the rate of inflation.

Final year students taking part in *The UK Graduate Careers Survey 2000* – the annual survey of finalists' career aspirations and expectations conducted by High Fliers Research – voted Andersen Consulting the year's top graduate employer and more finalists applied for jobs in management consulting than any other career area.

It is interesting to compare the results of that survey with the similar research carried out with the 'Class of 2010' earlier this year. In 2000 almost half of the top twenty employers that students thought offered the best opportunities for graduates were manufacturing or industrial companies. By contrast, just three of the organisations in this year's top twenty actually make anything – the list is dominated instead by accounting & professional services firms and public sector employers.

Typical salaries at *Top 100* graduate employers are £29,000 in 2010, more than 60% higher than the starting rates for graduates ten years ago. The average then was £18,000 and fewer than thirty-five employers in the UK offered new recruits packages of £25,000 or more.

Andersen Consulting is one of just three organisations that have made it to number one in *The Times Top 100 Graduate Employers* in the last ten years. The firm held on to the top spot for a further two years after 2000 and their success heralded a huge surge in popularity for careers in consulting. At its peak in 2001, almost one in six graduates applied for jobs in the sector.

In the year before the firm changed its name to Accenture, Andersen Consulting astutely introduced a new graduate package that included a £28,500 starting salary (a sky-high figure for graduates in 2000) and a much talked-about £10,000 bonus, helping to assure the firm's popularity, irrespective of its corporate branding.

By 2003, after two dismal years in graduate recruitment when vacancies for university-leavers dropped by more than a fifth following the

M&S YOUR

www.marksandspencer.com/gradcareers
We are M&S. Are you?

Whichever way you look at it, retail is demanding. So it takes a special sort of person to take their place on the M&S graduate programme. But if you love using your initiative to solve challenges of all shapes and sizes, there's simply nowhere better to build a rewarding long-term career.

Retail Management · HR · IT · Buying · Merchandising Product Technology & Design · Logistics · Business Placements And more...

A. Bitten off more than you can chew

B. Happiest with a full plate

terrorist attacks of 11th September 2001, the Civil Service was named Britain's leading graduate employer. A year later it was displaced by PricewaterhouseCoopers, the accounting and professional services firm formed from the merger of Price Waterhouse and Coopers & Lybrand in 1998. At the time, the firm was the largest private-sector recruiter of graduates, hiring over 1,000 trainees annually.

PricewaterhouseCoopers has now stayed at number one for a remarkable seven years running, increasing its share of the student vote from 5 per cent in 2004 to more than 10 per cent in 2007. The following year, the firm faced its stiffest competition yet from rivals Deloitte and retained the top ranking by just seven votes, but the margin between the two firms has grown in both 2009 and 2010.

PwC's reign as the leading employer represents a real renaissance for the entire accounting sector. Whereas a decade ago, a career in accountancy was widely regarded as a safe, traditional employment choice and the firms themselves were often derided as being 'dull', 'boring' or just 'bean-counters', today's profession is viewed in a very different light. The training required to become a chartered accountant is now seen as a prized business qualification and the sector's leading firms are regularly described as 'prestigious', 'dynamic' and 'international' by undergraduates looking for their first job after university.

Accountancy's transformation is underlined by the fact that fewer than 10 per cent of final year students opted for one of the top five accounting firms in *Top 100* of 1999, compared with the 22 per cent of votes polled by the 'Big Four' firms in this year's list.

A total of 191 different organisations have now appeared within *The Times Top 100 Graduate Employers* since its inception. Just fifty of these have made it into the rankings every year since 2000. The most consistent performers over this period have been the Civil Service, KPMG and Accenture each of which have never been lower than 8th place in the league table. Consumer goods company Procter & Gamble has also had a formidable record, appearing in every top ten until 2005, and GlaxoSmithKline, Ernst & Young, IBM and the Army have each remained within the top quarter of the list throughout.

PricewaterhouseCoopers and the now defunct accounting firm Arthur Andersen, are the only employers to have appeared within the top three throughout their time in the *Top 100*.

Tesco, Google and MI5 –The Security Service have each climbed more than sixty places within the *Top 100* over the last decade. Slaughter and May, Barclays Capital, Atkins and Citi have all reached the top half of the table, having moved up more than fifty positions in the rankings.

Other employers haven't been so successful. Ford, which was once rated as high as 14th, fell out of the list in 2006 after cancelling its graduate recruitment two years previously. And British Airways – ranked 12th in 2001 – dropped more than sixty places over the next eight years before leaving the rankings altogether in 2010.

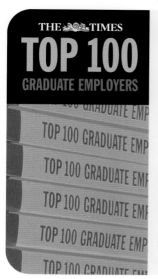

Movers & Shakers in the Top 100

Highest New Entries

2000	**Morgan Stanley** (34th)
2001	**Marconi** (36th)
2002	**Guinness UDV** (44th)
2003	**Asda** (40th)
2004	**Baker & McKenzie** (61st)
2005	**Penguin** (70th)
2006	**Fujitsu** (81st)
2007	**BDO Stoy Hayward** (74th)
2008	**Sky** (76th)
2009	**BDO Stoy Hayward** (68th)
2010	**Saatchi & Saatchi** (49th)

Highest Climbing Employers

2000	**Capital One** (up 32 places)
2001	**European Commission** (up 36 places)
2002	**WPP** (up 36 places)
2003	**Rolls-Royce** (up 37 places)
2004	**JPMorgan** (up 29 places)
2005	**Teach First** (up 22 places)
2006	**Google** (up 32 places)
2007	**Pfizer** (up 30 places)
2008	**Co-operative Group** (up 39 places)
2009	**Cadbury** (up 48 places)
2010	**Asda** (up 41 places)

Source **The UK Graduate Careers Survey 2000-2010**, High Fliers Research Ltd, based on interviews with 168,240 students.

SARA
RICHARDSON
SCIENCE

REBECCA
WHITE
HISTORY

VISHAL
PARMAR
MATHS

JASON
ARTHUR
ENGLISH

TAMSIN
ROBINSON
GEOGRAPHY

JONATHAN
SOBCZYK
CITIZENSHIP

Join in, stand out,
Teach First.

Registered charity no: 1098294

Question:
A class in a challenging school has 32 pupils.
13 of them are eligible for free school meals.
How many of them will go on to attend university?

Answer:
Just 2.

Is that ok with you? It's not with us – and we're doing something about it.
Over 2,500 outstanding graduates – people like you – have joined us and
become exceptional teachers and leaders, and transformed the life chances
of young people in challenging schools.

Now it's your turn.

www.teachfirst.org.uk

Thirty employers – including the Home Office, Nokia, Coca Cola, the Met Office, Apple and Nationwide – have the dubious record of having only been ranked in the *Top 100* once during the decade. Accounting firm BDO managed to be the highest new entry twice in both 2007 and 2009 but dropped out of the *Top 100* in the intervening year. And Marconi had the unusual distinction of being one of the highest-ever new entries in 36th place in 2001, only to vanish from the list entirely the following year.

One of the most spectacular ascendancies within the *Top 100* has been the rise and rise of Aldi which joined the list in 65th place in 2002 and rose to 3rd place in 2009, helped in part by its eye-catching remuneration package (currently £40,000 plus an Audi A4 car for new graduates).

And Teach First – the scheme which recruits graduates to work in the UK's most challenging schools for two years after university – has been another runaway success in the rankings. After appearing in the *The Times Top 100 Graduate Employers* as a new entry in 63rd place in 2003, the scheme has risen every year since – it is now ranked 7th and is set to recruit 730 graduates in 2011, its largest intake to date.

THE TIMES TOP 100 GRADUATE EMPLOYERS

Winners & Losers in the Top 100

Most Consistent Employers 2000-2010

	Highest Ranking	Lowest Ranking
Arthur Andersen *	**2nd** (2000-2001)	**3rd** (2002)
PricewaterhouseCoopers	**1st** (2004-2010)	**3rd** (2000-2001, 2003)
KPMG	**3rd** (2006-2008)	**7th** (2001)
Civil Service	**1st** (2003)	**6th** (2000-2001, 2008)
Accenture (formerly Andersen Consulting)	**1st** (2000-2002)	**8th** (2006, 2010)
Ernst & Young	**10th** (2009, 2010)	**20th** (2001)
IBM	**13th** (2000)	**23rd** (2008)
Procter & Gamble	**4th** (2000-2001)	**15th** (2007)
GlaxoSmithKline	**11th** (2000)	**22nd** (2002-2003)
Army	**4th** (2003)	**18th** (2007)

* Employer did not feature in the Top 100 every year between 2000 and 2010

Employers Climbing Highest 2000-2010

	New Entry Ranking	Highest Ranking
Tesco	**84th** (2000)	**13th** (2010)
Google	**85th** (2005)	**20th** (2009)
MI5 – The Security Service	**96th** (2007)	**33rd** (2010)
Aldi	**65th** (2002)	**3rd** (2009)
Atkins	**94th** (2004)	**37th** (2009)
Teach First	**63rd** (2003)	**7th** (2010)
Citi	**86th** (2000)	**30th** (2008)
Barclays Capital	**95th** (2004)	**43rd** (2010)
Slaughter and May	**90th** (2001)	**39th** (2010)
Oxfam	**95th** (2003)	**45th** (2006)

Employers Falling Furthest 2000-2010

	Highest Ranking	Lowest Ranking
British Airways	**12th** (2001)	**Not ranked** (2010)
Ford	**14th** (2002)	**Not ranked** (from 2006)
Reuters	**22nd** (2001)	**Not ranked** (from 2009)
Ministry of Defence	**35th** (2003)	**Not ranked** (2007)
AstraZeneca	**24th** (2003)	**88th** (2009)
Marconi	**36th** (2001)	**Not ranked** (from 2002)
Diageo	**37th** (2004)	**Not ranked** (2008-2009)
BT	**14th** (2000)	**75th** (2010)
ICI	**39th** (2000)	**Not ranked** (2004, from 2006)
Dstl	**43rd** (2001)	**Not ranked** (2007-2008, 2010)

Source **The UK Graduate Careers Survey 2000-2010**, High Fliers Research Ltd, based on interviews with 168,240 students.

THE TIMES
TOP 100
GRADUATE EMPLOYERS

Top 10 Graduate Employers 2000-2009

2000
1. Andersen Consulting (now Accenture)
2. Arthur Andersen
3. PricewaterhouseCoopers
4. Procter & Gamble
5. KPMG
6. Civil Service
7. Army
8. Unilever
9. Mars
10. BBC

2001
1. Accenture
2. Arthur Andersen
3. PricewaterhouseCoopers
4. Procter & Gamble
5. Goldman Sachs
6. Civil Service
7. KPMG
8. Unilever
9. Army
10. Mars

2002
1. Accenture
2. PricewaterhouseCoopers
3. Andersen (formerly Arthur Andersen)
4. Civil Service
5. Army
6. KPMG
7. Unilever
8. Procter & Gamble
9. Goldman Sachs
10. Mars

2003
1. Civil Service
2. Accenture
3. PricewaterhouseCoopers
4. Army
5. KPMG
6. HSBC
7. BBC
8. Procter & Gamble
9. NHS
10. Deloitte & Touche (now Deloitte)

2004
1. PricewaterhouseCoopers
2. Civil Service
3. Accenture
4. KPMG
5. NHS
6. BBC
7. Army
8. Procter & Gamble
9. HSBC
10. Deloitte

2005
1. PricewaterhouseCoopers
2. Civil Service
3. Accenture
4. KPMG
5. BBC
6. Deloitte
7. NHS
8. HSBC
9. Goldman Sachs
10. Procter & Gamble

2006
1. PricewaterhouseCoopers
2. Deloitte
3. KPMG
4. Civil Service
5. BBC
6. NHS
7. HSBC
8. Accenture
9. Procter & Gamble
10. Goldman Sachs

2007
1. PricewaterhouseCoopers
2. Deloitte
3. KPMG
4. Civil Service
5. BBC
6. NHS
7. Accenture
8. HSBC
9. Aldi
10. Goldman Sachs

2008
1. PricewaterhouseCoopers
2. Deloitte
3. KPMG
4. Accenture
5. NHS
6. Civil Service
7. BBC
8. Aldi
9. Teach First
10. Goldman Sachs

2009
1. PricewaterhouseCoopers
2. Deloitte
3. Aldi
4. Civil Service
5. KPMG
6. NHS
7. Accenture
8. Teach First
9. BBC
10. Ernst & Young

Source **The UK Graduate Careers Survey 2000-2009**, High Fliers Research Ltd, based on interviews with 152,126 students.

MIND THE GAP

BETWEEN HERE AND PAGE 238

Don't just fall into any old job. Go straight to the world-class opportunities on page 238.

MAYOR OF LONDON

Transport for London

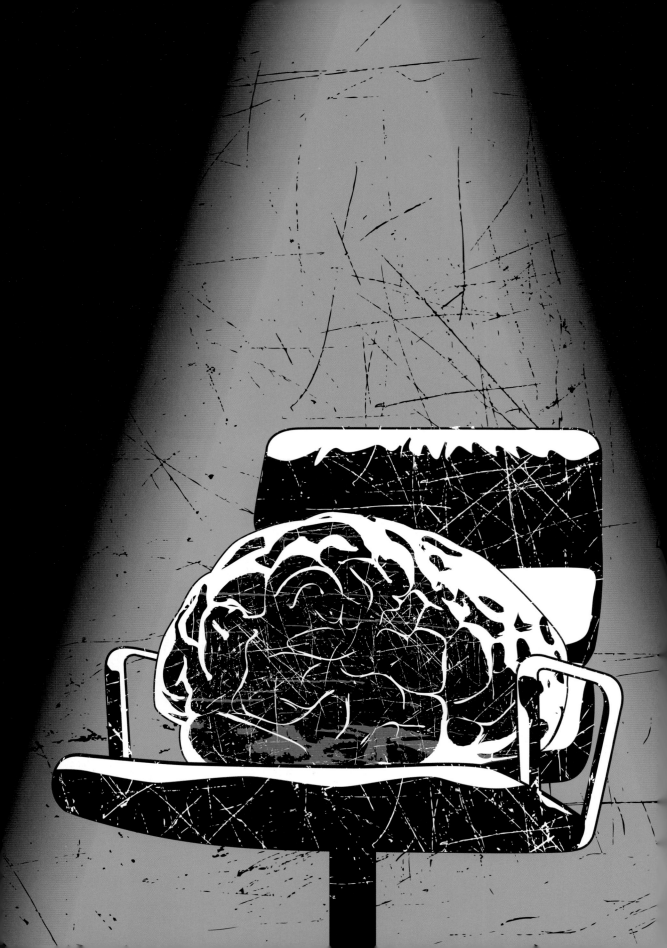

Your career is our specialist subject

milkround.com is the most widely-used graduate recruitment website at the UK's leading universities*. We have the jobs that answer your career questions.

milkround.com
Recruitment of the highest degree

If you're recruiting, find your mastermind at milkroundonline.com
*Source: The UK Graduate Careers Survey 2010

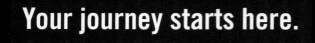

Your journey starts here.

thetimes.co.uk/career

Sign up now to
thetimes.co.uk
and get your first
30 days for only £1

thetimes.co.uk

THE TIMES
TOP 100
GRADUATE EMPLOYERS

Index

	Accountancy	Consulting	Engineering	Finance	General Management	Human Resources	Investment Banking	IT	Law	Logistics	Manufacturing	Marketing	Media	Purchasing	Research & Development	Retailing	Sales	Other
Accenture		●						●										
Airbus		●	●		●			●			●	●		●	●			
Aldi				●												●		
Allen & Overy									●									
Arcadia Group			●		●							●				●		
Army			●	●		●		●										
Arup		●	●															
Asda	●							●								●		
AstraZeneca			●	●				●				●			●			
Atkins	●	●	●															
BAE Systems			●	●				●			●							
Bain & Company		●																
Baker & McKenzie									●									
Balfour Beatty		●																
Bank of America Merrill Lynch				●		●	●	●				●					●	
Barclays Bank	●			●	●		●	●				●				●		
Barclays Capital				●			●	●	●			●						
BBC			●		●			●	●			●	●		●			
BDO	●																	
Bloomberg				●				●					●		●			●
BNP Paribas				●			●	●										
Boots				●				●				●						
Boston Consulting Group		●																
BP	●		●	●						●								
BT		●	●	●	●			●	●			●		●				
Cancer Research UK	●	●		●	●			●				●		●		●		
Centrica			●	●	●			●										
Citi			●	●		●	●	●										
Civil Service Fast Stream			●		●	●		●										
Clifford Chance									●									
Co-operative Group				●	●													
Credit Suisse				●			●	●										
Deloitte	●	●	●					●										
Diageo			●		●						●			●			●	
DLA Piper									●									
E.ON			●	●	●							●					●	
EDF Energy			●	●	●													○
Ernst & Young	●	●																
ExxonMobil			●	●				●							●	●		
Freshfields Bruckhaus Deringer									●									
GCHQ			●					●						●				○
GlaxoSmithKline			●	●				●			●	●		●	●			
Goldman Sachs	●			●			●	●										
Grant Thornton	●			●				●										
Herbert Smith									●									
Hogan Lovells									●									
HSBC			●	●	●		●				●		●				●	

Employer	Accountancy	Consulting	Engineering	Finance	General Management	Human Resources	Investment Banking	IT	Law	Logistics	Manufacturing	Marketing	Media	Purchasing	Research & Development	Retailing	Sales	Other
IBM	●	●	●	●	●			●									●	
J.P. Morgan				●			●	●										
Jaguar Land Rover	●		●	●				●		●	●			●	●		●	
John Lewis Partnership								●								●		
KPMG	●	●			●			●										
Kraft Foods			●	●				●			●	●			●		●	
L'Oréal				●								●			●		●	
Lidl					●									●		●		
Linklaters									●									
Lloyd's					●			●										
Lloyds Banking Group				●	●	●	●	●										
Marks & Spencer					●	●								●		●		
Mars			●	●	●									●	●			
McDonald's Restaurants					●											●		
McKinsey & Company		●																
Metropolitan Police	●			●	●	●		●				●	●					
MI5 – The Security Service			●	●		●		●	●					●				
Ministry of Defence			●															
Morgan Stanley				●			●	●										
Network Rail	●		●	●	●			●	●					●				
NGDP for Local Government					●													
NHS				●	●	●		●										
npower			●	●	●							●					●	
nucleargraduates		●	●	●	●	●			●					●				
Oxfam	●		●	●	●			●				●	●	●				
Penguin				●	●			●		●		●	●				●	
Police HPDS	●	●	●	●	●	●	●	●	●	●	●	●	●	●	●	●	●	
PricewaterhouseCoopers	●	●		●				●										
Procter & Gamble	●		●	●	●	●		●			●	●		●	●		●	
Rolls-Royce			●	●	●	●		●			●			●	●			
Royal Bank of Scotland Group	●		●	●	●	●	●	●				●		●		●		
Royal Navy			●	●	●			●		●				●				
Saatchi & Saatchi													●					
Sainsbury's			●	●	●			●		●		●		●		●		
Shell			●	●	●			●				●					●	
Siemens			●	●	●			●				●						
Sky	●				●			●				●	●					
Slaughter and May									●									
Sony					●			●				●	●		●		●	
Teach First	●	●	●	●	●	●	●	●	●	●		●		●		●	●	
Tesco	●	●	●	●	●			●		●	●	●		●		●		
Transport for London	●		●	●	●			●				●		●				
UBS	●			●		●		●										
Unilever			●	●	●			●				●			●		●	
Vodafone			●	●	●			●				●				●	●	
WPP Group												●	●					

accenture

High performance. Delivered.

www.accenture.com/top100

Vacancies for around
350-500 graduates in 2011

- ◼ **Consulting**
- ◼ **IT**

Starting salary for 2010
£31,500
Plus a £10,000 sign-on bonus.

Universities Accenture
plans to visit in 2010-11
Aston, Bath, Birmingham,
Bristol, Cambridge, Cardiff,
Durham, Edinburgh, Exeter,
Glasgow, Lancaster,
Leeds, Leicester, London,
Loughborough, Manchester,
Newcastle, Nottingham,
Oxford, Sheffield,
Southampton, St Andrews,
Strathclyde, Warwick, York
Please check with your university
careers service for details of events.

Application deadline
Year-round recruitment

Contact Details
☎ **0500 100 189**
Turn to page 248 now to request more
information or visit our new website at
www.top100graduateemployers.com

Achieve more.

accenture.com/top100

At Accenture, high performance is an everyday reality of working for a global management consulting, technology services and outsourcing company. This is a 190,000-strong firm that looks for graduates who want to build an exceptional career in the world of business and technology.

Accenture gives high-performing graduates everything they need to achieve more. A consulting career begins with exceptional training, including a two-week training course at Accenture's offices in Chicago within a graduate's first six months, and continues with the help of mentors, and a combination of classroom and online training courses. Working with big-name clients and with teams at all levels across the business, graduates gain exposure and responsibility.

In the Analyst Consulting Group, they work on projects across industries and specialisms to build strong business and technology expertise. This equips them with the insight to deliver commercial benefits in management consulting, systems integration and technology, often working alongside outsourcing teams. Consulting with Accenture offers a real breadth and depth of experience.

Accenture works with clients to help them become high-performing businesses, and it needs similar qualities in its graduates. Good academics are essential – a 2:1 or above and at least 340 UCAS points. This must be complemented by further evidence of high performance, be it through work experience or community involvement, a position of leadership or responsibility, a real interest in technology, and a genuine career focus.

Achieve more with Accenture. Find out about their graduate opportunities, as well as their schemes and placements, at accenture.com/top100

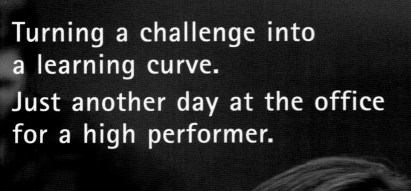

Turning a challenge into a learning curve.
Just another day at the office for a high performer.

© 2010 Accenture. All rights reserved.

Choose Accenture for a career where the variety of opportunities and challenges allows you to make a difference every day. A place where you can develop your potential and grow professionally, working alongside talented colleagues. The only place where you can learn from our unrivalled experience, while helping our global clients achieve high performance.

If this is your idea of a typical working day, then Accenture is the place to be.

Visit accenture.com/top100

• Consulting • Technology • Outsourcing

accenture

High performance. Delivered

AIRBUS
AN EADS COMPANY

Vacancies for around 50-80 graduates in 2011

- Engineering
- Finance
- Human Resources
- IT
- Logistics
- Manufacturing
- Purchasing
- Research & Development

Starting salary for 2011
£25,000

Universities that Airbus plans to visit in 2010-11

Bath, Bristol,
Liverpool, London,
Loughborough, Manchester,
Nottingham, Sheffield,
Southampton, Warwick
Please check with your university careers service for details of events.

Application deadline
See website for full details.

Contact Details
✉ airbusuk-grad@airbus.com

Turn to page 248 now to request more information or visit our new website at www.top100graduateemployers.com

Graduates with Airbus never know what they might get involved in, but they will be part of the world's leading aircraft manufacturer and a stimulating international environment.

Over 9,500 Airbus aircraft have been ordered by more than 300 customers and operators worldwide since the company first entered the market. Airbus Military has sold more than 1,000 aircraft; over 650 flying with over 100 operators across the world. Utilising advanced technologies, Airbus continues to incorporate innovation and eco-efficiency principles in the development of its newest aircraft programmes, the A350XWB and A400M, to improve efficiency and reduce environmental impact.

To stay at the top, Airbus needs to recruit the very best. Exciting challenges in engineering and business focused roles are open to talented people who want to join a vibrant business; helping to create an exciting, sustainable, eco-efficient future for aviation.

Collaborative and innovative graduates will enjoy the chance to develop their technical and leadership skills on the Airbus Direct Entry Graduate (DEG) programme. The structured programme helps develop a detailed knowledge of the chosen business function through placements in the UK and Europe, with strategic partners, customers and suppliers. Individual programmes can vary depending on the function joined.

Airbus DEGs have access to excellent focused training and support to help them achieve membership of professional institutions, further qualifications and long-term career planning. Involvement in education and community projects, to broaden personal and management skills is part of the programme and a work-life balance through flexible working is encouraged.

Careers with Airbus:
Our training, your commitment.

Airbus is a world-class aircraft manufacturer with the most modern and comprehensive family of airliners ranging in capacity from 100 to more than 500 seats. Employing approximately 52,000 people, drawn from over 80 nationalities, Airbus is a truly global organisation and offers a dynamic and diverse international working environment.

Every year we look for high-achieving graduates to join us either in permanent positions, or on our Direct Entry Graduate (DEG) or internship programmes.

The Airbus DEG Programme is a two or three-year training programme, with the opportunity of international placements. Graduates are trained in business and cultural awareness, personal effectiveness and technical understanding. Our graduates are also fully supported in gaining professional accreditation.

Our Internship programme provides exposure to a truly international culture. We offer numerous opportunities at our European sites throughout France, Germany, Spain and the UK. Our internship positions are generally of six or twelve months duration and designed so undergraduates can put into practice their theoretical knowledge and gain important industry experience.

For more information about the opportunities available and key application deadlines, please visit our website at **www.airbus-careers.com**

We are an Equal Opportunities Employer.

New Standards. Together.

Airbus is an EADS Company

AIRBUS

www.aldirecruitment.co.uk

Vacancies for around 50+ graduates in 2011

- General Management
- Retailing

Starting salary for 2011
£40,000
Rising to £61,000 after three years.

Universities that Aldi plans to visit in 2010-11
Aston, Bath, Birmingham, Bristol, Cardiff, Durham, Edinburgh, Exeter, Leeds, Leicester, Liverpool, Loughborough, Manchester, Newcastle, Nottingham, Nottingham Trent, Sheffield, Southampton, Strathclyde
Please check with your university careers service for details of events.

Application deadline
Year-round recruitment

Contact Details
Turn to page 248 now to request more information or visit our new website at www.top100graduateemployers.com

Aldi is well known for spotting outstanding graduates for its Aldi Management Programme. Those who stand out from the mix, go against the grain, push the envelope.

As one of the world's top retailers offering an excellent, market-leading package, Aldi has thousands of graduates applying for positions within its Management Programme. While most graduates achieve academically, Aldi wants to hear from those who have leadership experience. Graduates who have led a local or university sports team, carried out voluntary or charity work, taken a gap year, had a part-time job, or going the extra mile to reach individual potential is favoured by Aldi over first-class honours.

Those selected for the Aldi Management Programme have opportunities to fast-track their career from the classroom to the boardroom, with a programme aimed to prepare them for directorship after five years.

Selected graduates benefit from training in all aspects of retail management, from store operations through to financial administration, logistics and property management – and with around 7,000 stores worldwide, there are exciting international secondment opportunities.

Aldi's award-winning Management Programme gives graduates the opportunity to manage a store within weeks, progressing quickly to running a multi-million pound portfolio of stores with the skills mastered through training. Bottom line, Aldi stands out from other graduate programmes by giving its graduates high levels of responsibility from day one.

Put experience to task and visit www.aldirecruitment.co.uk.

Think we'd pay you £40,000 a year to tidy up trolleys in the car park?

Do you really think a company which is one of the largest, most successful privately owned businesses in the world would simply throw money at you? You'll only earn the sector-leading benefits package by taking on real responsibility – and showing us you have both unstoppable drive and a dogged determination to succeed. Yes, you will start at the bottom, on the shop floor. You will be tidying trolleys and stacking shelves. But, where better to learn the basics of retailing? Because, in just twelve months, we will expect you to be managing four to six Aldi stores... single-handedly. So, if you thought working for Aldi would be like working for any other supermarket, it might be worth thinking again. Then, if you think you've got what it takes, go to **www.aldirecruitment.co.uk**

Graduate
Area Manager
£40,000

rising to
£61,000
after three years

Fully expensed
Audi A4

Opportunity
for directorship
within 5 years

International
secondment
opportunities

ALLEN & OVERY

www.allenovery.com/careeruk

Vacancies for around 105 graduates in 2011
For training contracts starting in 2013

■ Law

Starting salary for 2011
£38,000

Universities Allen & Overy plans to visit in 2010-11
Bath, Belfast, Birmingham, Bristol, Cambridge, Cardiff, City, Dublin, Durham, East Anglia, Edinburgh, Exeter, Kent, Leeds, Leicester, London, Manchester, Newcastle, Northumbria, Nottingham, Oxford, Reading, Sheffield, Southampton, St Andrews, Warwick, York
Please check with your university careers service for details of events.

Application deadline
See website for full details.

Contact Details
✉ graduate.recruitment@allenovery.com
☎ 020 3088 0000

Turn to page 248 now to request more information or visit our new website at www.top100graduateemployers.com

Allen & Overy LLP is an international legal practice with approximately 5,000 people in 36 major centres worldwide. The practice's client list includes many of the world's top businesses, financial institutions and governments.

Allen & Overy is world renowned for the high quality of its banking, corporate and international capital markets advice, but also has major strengths in litigation and dispute resolution, employment and benefits, tax and real estate.

Within its broad range of expertise, the practice offers a training contract characterised by flexibility and choice. Training contracts are tailored for each trainee to ensure they have the best start to their career. Given the strength of the practice's international finance practice, trainees spend at least 12 months working in banking, corporate and international capital markets. There are also opportunities for trainees to undertake an international or client secondment in their second year of training. By working closely with trainers and other colleagues, trainees develop practical experience and enjoy a high level of early responsibility.

Vital to Allen & Overy's success is the way they approach work. Allen & Overy people enjoy what they do and want to employ individuals who can use their initiative while maintaining a professional, supportive and friendly working environment.

Allen & Overy recruits 105 trainee solicitors and 65 vacation students (winter and summer) each year. Applications are welcome from both law and non-law candidates. At least a 2.1 degree (or equivalent) should be predicted or acheived, with evidence of teamwork, leadership, motivation and problem-solving demonstrated.

ALLEN & OVERY

New frontiers

The world's financial markets are under closer scrutiny than ever before. In the wake of the financial crisis, some governments have moved to restrict short selling – betting that prices are going to fall. As a lawyer at Allen & Overy, what will that and other changes mean for your clients?

It will be down to you to help your clients negotiate the evolving regulatory environment – to structure products and transactions that continue to deliver commercial advantages within a legal framework that is itself changing. You will be their guide, providing ideas and solving problems at the frontiers of business and law.

Careers at Allen & Overy are about providing clear, insightful legal advice, working collaboratively – with colleagues and clients – and striving to deliver outstanding results. Your role will be to bring clarity to complex issues and support decision-making at the highest level, enabling our clients – some of the most ambitious companies in the world – to address challenges that will define their futures. In today's legal and business landscape, our clients expect intelligent commercial advice delivered consistently and globally. Join us and be part of our success.

Start at the top.

A Career in Law

www.allenovery.com/careeruk

Allen & Overy means Allen & Overy LLP and/or its affiliated undertakings

▲ Arcadia Group Limited

www.arcadiagroup.co.uk/careers

Vacancies for around 200-250 graduates in 2011

- Finance
- Human Resources
- Logistics
- Purchasing
- Retailing

▲ Arcadia Group Limited

Starting salary for 2011
£17,850-£23,000

Universities that the Arcadia Group plans to visit in 2010-11
Please check with your university careers service for details of events.

Application deadline
Year-round recruitment
See website for full details.

Contact Details
Turn to page 248 now to request more information or visit our new website at www.top100graduateemployers.com

Arcadia Group is the UK's largest privately owned fashion retailer with over 28,000 employees, 2,700 outlets and over 400 international stores in 29 different countries. Arcadia's portfolio of brands include seven of the high street best known fashion brands – Burton, Dorothy Perkins, Evans, Miss Selfridge, Topman, Topshop and Wallis – along with the shopping concept Outfit.

Arcadia offers a wide variety of different careers for graduates and trainees. London based opportunities include: Buying, Merchandising, Distribution, Finance and HR. Their Retail Management programme offers candidates nation wide opportunities.

Arcadia's people play a vital part in their success and they're committed to supporting the development of their teams. In all roles, graduates will benefit from on the job competency based training and core skill workshops.

Graduates and trainees are rewarded with a competitive salary, up to 25 days holiday, bonus, membership of the group pension scheme, sponsorship of professional qualifications and an attractive 25% discount on products from Arcadia stores!

Arcadia are always on the look out for the most commercial, passionate, success driven candidates that have a passion for customer service and fashion retail.

Arcadia's Buying, Merchandising and Distribution roles are recruited all year round, while Finance, HR and Retail Management programmes are open for applications from early September.

▲ **Arcadia Group Limited**

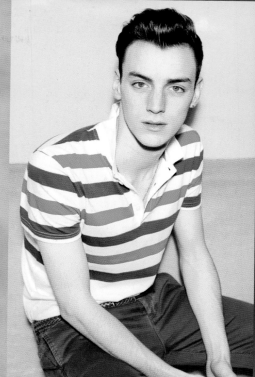

ARCADIA CAREERS

Are you confident and commercial?
Do you have a passion for fashion retail?
Want to be at the heart of a business
where talent is recognised?

Working for the Arcadia Group is not like
working for any other retailer.

Our people benefit from the opportunity
to develop their career and move
between brands – without ever having
to change employer. Whether you're
working in a store or at our head office,
there's no mistaking that you're at
the heart of a fast moving, innovative
fashion retail group.

We offer a wide variety of different
careers for graduates and trainees in
both our London head office and our
stores. London based opportunities
include: Buying, Merchandising,
Distribution, Finance and HR. Our
Retail Management programme offers
candidates nationwide opportunities.

For more information please visit:
www.arcadiagroup.co.uk/careers

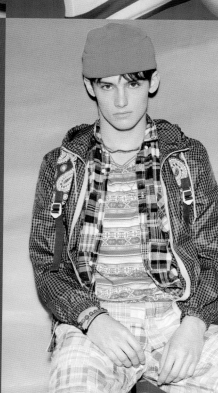

BHS   **BURTON**   DOROTHY PERKINS   *evans*   *Miss Selfridge*   **OUTFIT**   TOPSHOP   **TOPMAN**   *wallis*

ARMY
BE THE BEST
REGULAR & TERRITORIAL

Vacancies for around 750 graduates in 2011

- Engineering
- Finance
- General Management
- Human Resources
- IT
- Logistics

Starting salary for 2011
£24,615

Universities that the Army plans to visit in 2010-11
Please check with your university careers service for details of events.

Application deadline
Year-round recruitment

Contact Details
Turn to page 248 now to request more information or visit our new website at www.top100graduateemployers.com

Being an Army Officer is a graduate career with a difference – from commanding a platoon of over 30 soldiers preparing for operations one week to organising a team training event the next, the British Army trains graduates to become some of the best leaders in the world.

As one of the largest most respected graduate employers, the Army offers unrivalled training and development to graduates of all disciplines, enhancing management and leadership potential and providing the skills and self-confidence to excel in the Army and, later on, in other careers.

Graduates start their Officer training at the Royal Military Academy Sandhurst (RMAS) where they learn all aspects of soldiering, as well as gain transferable skills in communication and leadership.

On completion of training at RMAS, they will join their Regiment or Corps where they will undergo further specialist training for their chosen occupation. Subsequently, Officers can also choose to study for recognised qualifications to further boost their CVs.

As well as offering variety, the Army offers continuous professional learning opportunities, great promotional prospects, unrivalled travel, sporting and adventure opportunities as well as benefits such as competitive pay and six weeks paid holiday per year.

The Army has approximately 750 graduate officer vacancies per annum, graduates should search 'Army jobs' to find out if they have got what it takes for a career in the Army. The Graduate offer salary is £29,586 on completion of training with good promotional prospects to follow.

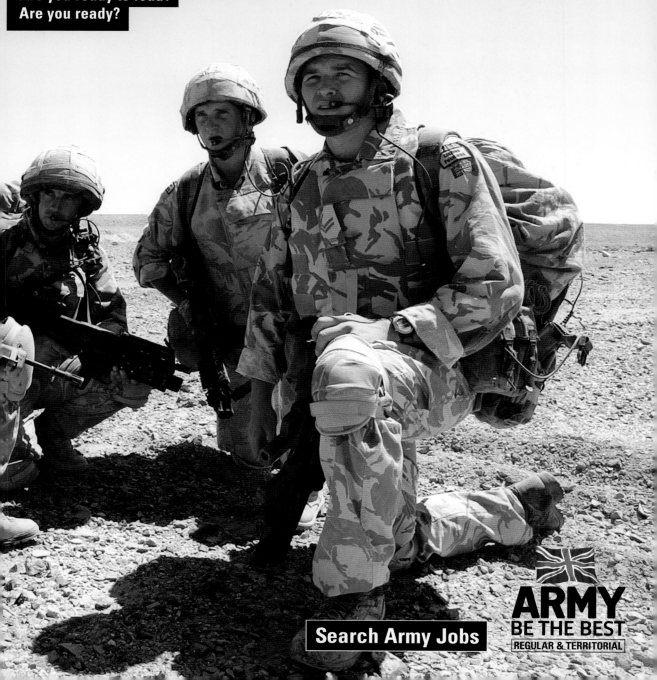

WHERE TO NEXT?

They'll look to you for guidance.
They'll look to you for strength.
They'll put themselves in your hands.
Are you ready to lead?
Are you ready?

Search Army Jobs

ARMY
BE THE BEST
REGULAR & TERRITORIAL

ARUP

www.arup.com

**Vacancies for around
100 graduates in 2011**

Consulting
Engineering
Finance

Vacancies also available in Europe,
the USA and Asia.

Starting salary for 2011
£21,000-£26,000

**Universities that Arup
plans to visit in 2010-11**
Bath, Birmingham, Bristol,
Cambridge, City, Durham,
Edinburgh, Heriot-Watt,
Leeds, Liverpool, London,
Manchester, Newcastle,
Nottingham, Sheffield,
Strathclyde, Warwick
Please check with your university
careers service for details of events.

Application deadline
Year-round recruitment

Contact Details
✉ gradrec@arup.com
Turn to page 248 now to request more
information or visit our new website at
www.top100graduateemployers.com

Arup is a global firm of designers, engineers, planners
and business consultants providing a diverse range of
professional services to clients around the world.
Arup's innovative and fully-integrated approach brings
their full complement of skills and knowledge to bear on
any given design problem.

They exert a significant influence on the built environment and are the
creative force behind many of the world's most innovative and sustainable
designs. Examples of Arup projects are: the Beijing National Stadium and
Water Cube, Sydney Opera House, the Millennium Bridge, the Swiss Re
Headquarters and the City of Manchester Stadium.

Arup has over 9,000 staff worldwide in 92 offices in more than 37 countries.
At any one time, they have over 10,000 projects running concurrently.

A commitment to the environment and the communities being worked in
has always been at the heart of the Arup ethos. It defines their approach
to their work, to their clients and collaborators, and to each other.

Arup recruits over 100 graduates in the UK every year and has graduate
vacancies in acoustics, architecture, bridges, building design,
communications and systems, environment, fire, finance, geotechnics and
tunnelling, highways, intelligent transport systems, lighting, management
consultancy, materials, quantity surveying, rail, risk management, site
development, town planning, transaction advice, transport planning
and water.

For further information please visit www.arup.com

Who'd have thought something as vast and complex as Beijing's Water Cube could be inspired by something as small and simple as soap bubbles? We would have. And we did. The result was yet another pioneering structure powered by the vision and imagination of some of the finest design, planning and engineering minds anywhere on earth. And for our next big thought bubble, brainwave or eureka moment? Who knows? Keep your head up, your eyes open and your brain whirring and maybe, just maybe, it'll be yours. Visit **www.arup.com**

ARUP

Inspiration, everywhere you look

Acoustics
Architecture
Bridges
Building design
Communications and systems
Environment
Fire
Finance
Geotechnics and tunnelling
Highways
Intelligent transport systems
Lighting
Management consultancy
Materials
Quantity surveying
Rail
Risk management
Site development
Town planning
Transaction advice
Transport planning
Water

FROM BATHING TO BEIJING.

Water Cube: Photography by Martin Saunders

ASDA

asda.jobs/graduates

Vacancies for around 45-50 graduates in 2011

- Accountancy
- Finance
- General Management
- IT
- Logistics
- Purchasing
- Retailing

Starting salary for 2011
£23,000

Universities that Asda plans to visit in 2010-11
Bradford, Brunel, City, Durham, Leeds, Liverpool, Manchester, Nottingham, Oxford, Sheffield, Warwick
Please check with your university careers service for details of events.

Application deadline
3rd January 2011

Contact Details
Turn to page 248 now to request more information or visit our new website at www.top100graduateemployers.com

Part of the Wal-Mart family, Asda is one of the UK's fastest growing and most successful retailers. The business employs over 170,000 people across 400 stores, 23 depots and its Leeds-based head office, Asda House.

Asda graduates play a pivotal role in exceeding the expectations of more than 17 million customers every week. Graduates can forge careers in everything from Store Management, leading and inspiring up to 1000 colleagues every day, to Trading, working in partnership with suppliers from across the world to deliver everyday low prices. Asda offers numerous opportunities to gain challenging, varied and rewarding experiences, as well as the chance to deliver projects that change the lives of customers, every day.

Operating as one team, everyone at Asda is committed to saving customers money. Asda prides itself on a unique culture, which encourages all colleagues to reach their full potential as quickly as possible – and to enjoy themselves along the way. Achievements are recognised and feedback is valued and encouraged.

Asda welcomes applications from any degree discipline. Its graduate programme covers Retail Management, Ecommerce, Finance, Supply Chain, IT Solutions, Distribution Management and Trading.

Whatever the ambition, graduates at Asda go further, higher, faster. They take on meaningful responsibility from day one in order to make a real contribution, all while developing the skills to become future leaders at Asda.

ASDA
SAVING
YOU MONEY EVERY DAY

Customer focusing.
Store running.
Sleeve rolling.
Problem solving.
Negotiating.
Deal making.
Adrenaline pumping.
Deadline beating.

(And all to save money on your beans on toast)

At Asda, every single day, every colleague goes out of their way to save our customers money. And whether you work in Retail Management, Distribution, Trading, Ecommerce, Finance, IT Solutions Management, Supply Chain or Marketing, while you're helping us deliver great value, you'll be developing at a pace that's second to none. A career at Asda can take you further, higher, faster than other graduate careers, and you'll find every 100mph day challenging, but ultimately rewarding. It's not your average day, every day.

For more information on our Graduate Programmes, go to www.**ASDA**.jobs/graduates

(Like grease lightning)

Further. Higher. Faster. Asda

AstraZeneca

Vacancies for around 15-25 graduates in 2011

- Engineering
- Finance
- IT
- Logistics
- Marketing
- Purchasing
- Research & Development

Starting salary for 2011
£25,000-£28,000

Universities AstraZeneca plans to visit in 2010-11
Please check with your university careers service for details of events.

Application deadline
Year-round recruitment

Contact Details
Turn to page 248 now to request more information or visit our new website at www.top100graduateemployers.com

As one of the world's leading pharmaceutical companies, AstraZeneca turns great ideas into innovative medicines which make a real difference to people's lives.

The company's excellent reputation and diversity of graduate opportunities make them the natural choice for candidates from a science background.

However, their strengths in manufacturing and commerce mean they can also provide challenges to graduates from other disciplines. Whatever their degree subject, graduates will be excited by the quality and diversity of opportunity.

Programmes are designed to progress careers through an integrated range of flexible training activities and blended learning ideas.

From day-one induction and personal mentoring to management and global leadership programmes, AstraZeneca provides the resources and support graduates need to reach their full potential; while cross-functional moves, secondments and international assignments can broaden the experience.

It's a performance-based culture with competitive salaries and bonuses that are linked to overall progress. But they also believe that quality of life and quality of work go hand in hand. That's why they actively pursue opportunities for flexible working arrangements.

Core benefits include a minimum level of pension contribution and healthcare provision, and the additional range of 'rewards options' is considerable. But these are benefits that people tend to appreciate further down the line. What probably excites graduates more at this stage is the opportunity to develop their skills within a truly global business that's setting the standards in an industry rich in challenges and rewards.

Working here means opportunities to create, solve, challenge and improve.

If there's one thing that binds everyone together around the world, it's our health. Whatever background we come from, lasting wellbeing is always our top priority.

AstraZeneca is one of the world's leading biopharmaceutical companies, and we know that our drugs are only one part of the solution. Our 62,000 employees are actively engaged with communities and healthcare professionals around the globe, looking for new, innovative ways to solve people's problems. Making the connections that lead to a healthier world.

astrazenecacareers.com

ΛTKINS

www.atkinsglobal.com/graduates/times

Vacancies for around 100 graduates in 2011

- Accountancy
- Consulting
- Engineering
- Finance

Starting salary for 2011
£20,000-£28,000

Universities that Atkins plans to visit in 2010-11

Aberdeen, Bath, Belfast, Birmingham, Bristol, Cambridge, Cardiff, Durham, Glasgow, Heriot-Watt, Leeds, Liverpool, London, Loughborough, Manchester, Nottingham, Oxford, Sheffield, Southampton, Strathclyde, Surrey, Warwick
Please check with your university careers service for details of events.

Application deadline
See website for full details.

Contact Details

✉ graduates@atkinsglobal.com
☎ 0121 483 5089

Turn to page 248 now to request more information or visit our new website at www.top100graduateemployers.com

Atkins is the UK's largest engineering and design consultancy, using the depth and breadth of their expertise to respond to the world's most technically challenging infrastructure projects – none more urgent than creating a low carbon future. In fact, Atkins is the first engineering consultancy to be awarded the Carbon Trust Standard in the construction and building management sector.

Atkins is also proud to be the engineering design expert behind London 2012. As the first official engineering design services provider to an Olympic Games, Atkins is leading the sector and will showcase the London 2012 Games as a feat of engineering excellence.

Then there's the big one: the International Thermonuclear Experimental Reactor (ITER). It's one of the most ambitious science projects of our time and, as the architect engineer, Atkins will help create a device capable of generating ten times the power it consumes. In addition to pioneering new technology, Atkins continues to find new ways of harnessing the power of nature – like Anaconda, a 200-metre snake-like tube that creates energy by pulsing under the sea.

Atkins doesn't just help their clients become energy efficient. Their Bristol office has impressive environmental credentials of its own, rated 'Excellent' by the industry leading measure BREEAM (or Building Research Establishment's Environmental Assessment Method to give it its full title).

Whether it's engineering new infrastructures or finding new, sustainable ways to power them, Atkins plan, design and enable solutions for the world.

ATKINS

The official engineering design services
provider for the London 2012 Games

Aerospace
Building Design
Communication & Systems
Conventional Power
Defence
Environment
Finance
Geotechnics & Tunnelling
Highways
Intelligent Transport Systems
Management Consultancy
Nuclear Power
Oil & Gas
Rail & Metro
Transport Planning
Water

Aim higher

Join our Graduate Development Programme and together we'll build a brighter future for everyone.

Instead of leading you down a set career path, we'll open doors by giving you choices about how your career unfolds and providing a breadth of projects to gain experience on. And as one of the leading infrastructure consultancies, we're well placed to invest in your development and offer the career opportunities you're looking for.

If you share our boundless curiosity and drive to improve the world in which we all live, work and play, it's a chance to become an expert in whatever inspires you most.

Make the story of your career a more interesting one. To find out more and apply, visit **www.atkinsglobal.com/graduates/times**

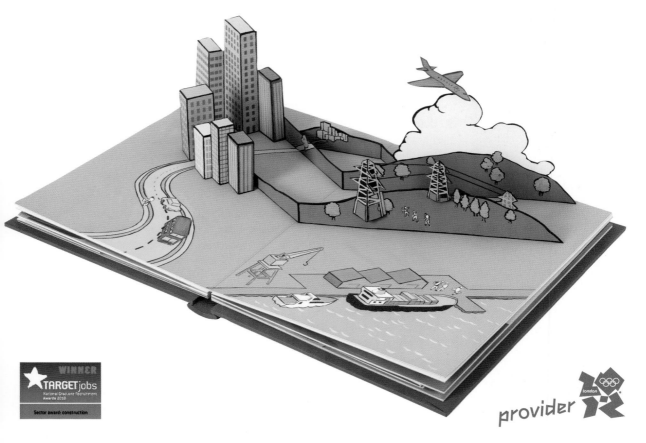

WINNER
TARGETjobs
National Graduate Recruitment
Awards 2010

Sector award: construction

provider

Plan Design Enable

© Atkins Ltd except where stated otherwise. The Atkins logo, the "open A" device and the strapline "Plan Design Enable" are trademarks of Atkins Ltd. The official Emblem of the London Organising Committee of the Olympic Games and Paralympic Games Ltd is © 2007 The London Organising Committee of the Olympic Games and Paralympic Games Limited. All rights reserved.

BAE SYSTEMS

REAL PERFORMANCE. REAL ADVANTAGE.

www.baesystems.com/graduates

Vacancies for around 200 graduates in 2011

- Engineering
- Finance
- Human Resources
- IT
- Manufacturing

CALLING ALL OF NATURE'S GREAT PERFORMERS.

Starting salary for 2011
£24,000-£28,000

Universities BAE Systems plans to visit in 2010-11

Bath, Belfast, Bristol, Brunel, Cambridge, Cardiff, Durham, Edinburgh, Glasgow, Heriot-Watt, Kent, Lancaster, Leeds, Liverpool, Loughborough, Manchester, Newcastle, Nottingham, Oxford, Sheffield, Southampton, Strathclyde, Surrey, Warwick, York

Please check with your university careers service for details of events.

Application deadline
Year-round recruitment
Early application is advised.

Contact Details
Turn to page 248 now to request more information or visit our new website at www.top100graduateemployers.com

When looking for high performance, nothing beats the systems found in nature. Three billion years of evolution. That's the inspiration behind so much of what BAE Systems do. Join them and become part of Europe's largest defence, security and aerospace company with over 107,000 employees' worldwide and reported sales of £22.4 billion.

BAE Systems believes in being the best. Doing everything better than before. After all, it's in their nature. So it's only natural they should look for graduates who'll do better. Go further and achieve more. Unlike many other schemes, BAE Systems' graduates are recruited directly into a business unit. That means they'll only work in areas that suit their ambitions.

Few organisations can offer opportunities as exciting and challenging in the fields of business, engineering and finance. Whether it's the Graduate Development Framework (GDF), Finance Leader Development Programme (FLDP) or the Sigma Leadership Programme (SLP), all of them provide a mix of training and experiences that will help graduates become great performers.

Whichever area of the business graduates initially join on the programme; they will be encouraged and supported to develop their natural potential. This could mean further study towards relevant professional qualifications, for which BAE Systems will provide all the resources and support needed.

BAE Systems won't hold graduates' hands. Successful applicants need to plan, drive and continue to set and achieve their own ambitious goals. It's their career, and they'll be responsible for taking it to the heights they want to reach.

CALLING ALL OF NATURE'S GREAT PERFORMERS.

The dolphin. The ultimate listening device. Inspired by a dolphin's sonar, our Astute submarine sonar system has the world's largest number of hydrophones, giving it the biggest ears of any sonar system in service today. In fact, the perfect performance in nature is a great source of inspiration for our people, who are always looking to develop the most effective defence, aerospace and security systems on earth.

BUSINESS | ENGINEERING | FINANCE

baesystems.com/graduates

BAE SYSTEMS

REAL PERFORMANCE. REAL ADVANTAGE.

BAIN & COMPANY

Vacancies for no fixed quota **of graduates in 2011**

Consulting

Starting salary for 2011
£Competitive

**Universities that
Bain & Company
plans to visit in 2010-11**

Bristol, Cambridge,
Dublin, Durham, London,
Oxford, Warwick
Please check with your university
careers service for details of events.

Application deadline
8th November 2010

Contact Details
✉ GraduateRecruiting.London
@Bain.com

Turn to page 248 now to request more
information or visit our new website at
www.top100graduateemployers.com

Bain & Company is one of the world's leading strategy consulting firms ranked #1 'Best Firm to Work For' by Consulting Magazine for the past eight years.

Bain works with top management teams to tackle their key issues and are focused on results and delivering substantial, lasting financial impact to their clients.

As Associate Consultants (AC) graduates will be responsible for helping to solve Bain's clients' critical issues and will learn how to develop and implement practical solutions. Bain offers the best practical business experience there is: quite simply, graduates will learn how to make companies more valuable.

Bain also offers unparalleled flexibility – ACs have the opportunity to pursue an MBA sponsored by Bain, go on an externship or take a leave of absence to do charity work or travel.

Throughout a career at Bain, graduates will have excellent training. The first year starts with two weeks of training in the London office and a further two week global training programme in Cape Cod, Massachusetts where they will train alongside international colleagues. Bain is a meritocracy – there is no fixed length of time that a person should stay at a particular level. Progression is driven purely by performance, not by tenure.

The people at Bain are dynamic, entrepreneurial and thrive on early responsibility. Bain looks for exceptional graduates and postgraduates from any degree discipline who demonstrate strong analytical and communication skills, initiative, leadership and teamwork.

People.
Passion.
Results.

Bain & Company is one of the world's leading strategy consulting firms, ranked #1 Best Firm to Work for by Consulting Magazine for the past eight years. Our clients include some of the most successful global companies and private equity firms.

Bain people are dynamic, entrepreneurial and thrive on early responsibility.

We look for exceptional graduates and post-graduates from any degree discipline who demonstrate strong analytical skills, initiative, leadership and teamwork.

To find out more visit **www.joinbain.com**

BAIN & COMPANY

BAKER & M°KENZIE

www.multiplyingyourpotential.co.uk

Vacancies for around 38 graduates in 2011
For training contracts starting in 2013

Law

Starting salary for 2011
£37,500

Universities that Baker & McKenzie plans to visit in 2010-11
Birmingham, Bristol, Cambridge, Durham, Edinburgh, Leeds, London, Manchester, Nottingham, Oxford, St Andrews, York
Please check with your university careers service for details of events.

Application deadline
Law: 31st July 2011
Non-Law: 31st March 2011

Contact Details
✉ multiplyingyourpotential @bakernet.com
Turn to page 248 now to request more information or visit our new website at www.top100graduateemployers.com

Baker & McKenzie in London offers unparalleled opportunities to become a first class lawyer in the world's largest global law firm. With a network covering 67 offices in 39 countries and a presence in every important financial and commercial centre worldwide, the Firm is able to attract the highest quality multi-jurisdictional clients.

There is no Baker & McKenzie template to which all trainees must conform. The Firm is looking for people who share its international outlook and who want to develop their legal career in a challenging, rewarding and friendly environment. In return, the Firm provides exceptional training to enable graduates to multiply their potential.

The two-year Training Programme commences with an interactive and practical induction which is geared towards enabling successful applicants to start making an immediate contribution to the Firm. There are four six-month 'seats' which include one in the Corporate department and one contentious seat. Trainees are given early responsibility on high profile transactions and as well as gaining international exposure in their day-to-day work, the Firm runs secondment programmes for trainees and associates. Recent secondees have been to Brussels, Moscow, Hong Kong and Tokyo.

Baker & McKenzie's commitment to training begins even before starting a career with the Firm through London and International Summer Placements. These provide the opportunity of experiencing the work and culture of the Firm, with the International Placement also including time spent in one of the Firm's international offices.

Your perspective ✕ Our world

Multiplying your potential

"It's exactly how I wanted my career to develop. I'm working in a global, multi-cultural setting, on high quality deals with blue-chip clients, and all within a welcoming and supportive environment. It's about helping me to develop my experience and enabling me to be the best lawyer I can be."

Emily Carlisle, Associate, Corporate

Do you want to multiply your potential?
www.multiplyingyourpotential.co.uk

BAKER & McKENZIE

Balfour Beatty

www.balfourbeatty.com/graduates

Vacancies for around 150 graduates in 2011

Engineering

Starting salary for 2011
£Competitive

Universities that Balfour Beatty plans to visit in 2010-11

Bath, Birmingham, Bristol, Cambridge, Cardiff, Edinburgh, Glasgow, Heriot-Watt, Leeds, Liverpool, Loughborough, Manchester, Newcastle, Northumbria, Nottingham, Plymouth, Reading, Sheffield, Southampton, Warwick
Please check with your university careers service for details of events.

Application deadline
See website for full details.

Contact Details
Turn to page 248 now to request more information or visit our new website at www.top100graduateemployers.com

Balfour Beatty is a world-class infrastructure services business. They deliver services essential to the creation and care of infrastructure assets, including investment, project design, financing and management, engineering and construction, and facilities management. The company is structured into four divisions: professional services, construction services, support services and infrastructure investments. The professional services division, Parsons Brinckerhoff, was acquired in 2009.

Each year Balfour Beatty recruits approximately 150 graduates from a variety of disciplines: engineering (civil, electrical, mechanical, building services); building/construction management; commercial management/quantity surveying; environmental; transportation planning; business; and management. Whether designing, delivering or maintaining awe-inspiring projects, graduates are able to create a lasting impression.

Balfour Beatty is delighted to have been ranked in The Times Top 100 Graduate Employers 2010 as the second highest new entrant. A major factor in this achievement is the excellent training and support – something that's strengthened by the sheer scale and scope of projects in which graduates can have hands-on involvement.

Balfour Beatty's global projects span the private and public sectors, and touch every part of life. For ambitious graduates they offer more options, responsibility and insight into every part of the infrastructure lifecycle.

Graduates who are looking to make a sustainable, long-term and positive impact are sure to thrive at Balfour Beatty.

Balfour Beatty

CREATE A LASTING IMPRESSION

BLACKFRIARS STATION

Graduate Opportunities

When you join Balfour Beatty as a graduate, you embark on a career that will create a lasting impression. On the world around you. On the people who live in it. On you. That's because we're an industry leader operating across the entire infrastructure lifecycle. A company that has grown to become the first choice for more customers and more graduates. And a place where you will work on the most awe-inspiring, complex and essential projects out there.

To find out more about the wide range of graduate opportunities we have to offer, go to

www.balfourbeatty.com/graduates

Sliding a 350-tonne span into space

Transforming the Victorian Blackfriars rail bridge into a structure fit for 21st century London is just one of the projects we're involved in right now.

London's only cross-river station

We're completely redeveloping the existing station and extending its platforms so that they cross the Thames, allowing passengers access to both sides of the river.

Barging in

To keep traffic off London's crowded roads, steelwork is being delivered by river, via a one hundred tonne barge-mounted crane.

WINNER
TARGETjobs
National Graduate Recruitment
Awards 2010

Sector award: quantity surveying and building surveying

Bank of America
Merrill Lynch

bankofamerica.com/campusrecruiting

**Vacancies for around
450 graduates in 2011**

- Finance
- Human Resources
- Investment Banking
- IT
- Marketing
- Research & Development
- Sales

Vacancies also available in Europe.

Starting salary for 2011
£Competitive

**Universities that Bank of
America Merrill Lynch
plans to visit in 2010-11**
Please check with your university
careers service for details of events.

Application deadline
12th November 2010

Contact Details
Turn to page 248 now to request more
information or visit our new website at
www.top100graduateemployers.com

Bank of America Merrill Lynch is part of Bank of America,
one of the world's largest financial institutions serving
individuals, small and middle market businesses and large
corporations with a range of banking, investing, asset
management and other financial and risk-management products
and services. The company has relationships with 99 percent
of the U.S. Fortune 500 and nearly 96 percent of the Fortune
Global 500; it prides itself on offering an array of world-class
products and world-class service to clients.

The company is ideally placed to offer the scope and opportunities the cream of
graduate talent deserves. Full-time and internship programmes are available in
these areas: Global Markets, Corporate & Investment Banking, Capital Markets,
Global Wealth & Investment Management, Research, Treasury Management,
Corporate & Financial Institutions Debt Products, Operations & Middle Office,
Risk Management, Technology, Human Resources and Card Services.

Graduates who join the organisation gain a breadth of knowledge and
experience and are positioned for great growth opportunities. They will work
alongside professionals who are leaders in the industry and have skilled mentors
who are committed to developing talent. In addition, they will be offered
unlimited opportunities to develop their abilities and grow professionally through
a variety of structured training courses.

Strong academic qualifications and quantitative skills are important for
success in the company's analyst programmes. Equally important are initiative,
strategic and creative thinking, communication skills and a genuine interest in
the financial markets.

Agility

Your unique talents and hard work make success look easy.

Face challenges with confidence. Nimbly navigate every obstacle in your path. It's that unique quality that's positioned you where you are today. And it's what we value at Bank of America. Join our team, and we'll open your career path and give you new opportunities to take the possible and make it real. We'll solicit your input and provide training, mentorship, and support to boost your aspirations to a global level. And as part of the world's leading financial institution, you can create the kind of opportunity that begets greater opportunity and bigger impact than you ever imagined.

Set opportunity in motion.

bankofamerica.com/**campusrecruiting**

© 2010 Bank of America Corporation. All rights reserved.

Bank of America
Merrill Lynch

 **BARCLAYS**

barclays-graduates.co.uk/TT100

Vacancies for around
100+ graduates in 2011

- Accountancy
- Finance
- General Management
- Human Resources
- IT
- Marketing
- Retailing

Vacancies also available in Europe
and elsewhere in the world.

Starting salary for 2011
£Competitive

Universities that Barclays
plans to visit in 2010-11
Aberdeen, Bath,
Birmingham, Bristol,
Cambridge, Cardiff, City,
Durham, Edinburgh, Exeter,
Glasgow, Lancaster,
Leeds, Leicester, London,
Loughborough, Newcastle,
Nottingham, Oxford,
Southampton, St Andrews,
Strathclyde, Surrey,
Warwick, York
Please check with your university
careers service for details of events.

Application deadline
31st December 2010

Contact Details
Turn to page 248 now to request more
information or visit our new website at
www.top100graduateemployers.com

Why settle for the small time?

Barclays is best known as one of the UK's top high street banks. The full picture, however, is much bigger. This is an enormously broad and far-reaching global financial services organisation, operating in over 50 countries and serving more than 48 million customers and clients worldwide. Global Retail Banking (GRB) alone provides retail banking and credit card services to 37 million of those customers from 3,500 distribution points in 21 countries. Welcome to big-time banking.

The sheer scale and ambition level of GRB opens up a diverse array of opportunities for graduates interested in global leadership careers. There's a General Leadership Programme alongside Functional Leadership Programmes in Human Resources, Marketing and Products, Credit Risk, Operations, Technology, Finance and Tax. Barclays are building a very different bank. They have a bold vision to make 'Lives Much Easier' for their customers, and are building a group of global leaders who can turn this vision into reality.

Barclays Future Leadership Development Programmes offer a well structured, fast-track route to a global careers path and prepares graduates to become future leaders within the bank. With that in mind, these are opportunities for a particular kind of high-achieving graduate. Ambitious, inquisitive, academically astute and commercially aware, they'll be keen to make their mark, have their say and improve on what's gone before.

By doing so, they'll take their place at the heart of Barclays plans for the years ahead. The skills, influence and wider business understanding they build will stand them in good stead to explore Group-wide prospects, as they help to keep the bank at the forefront of the global financial markets.

See more. Be more.

Elevating viewpoints. Expanding horizons. Exceeding expectations. Here at Barclays, genuine powerhouse of the financial services world, we do the lot. With 144,000 people in over 50 countries, we have the depth and breadth to take your future in any number of incredible directions. But only as long as you have the vision and ambition to do the same for us. After all, we don't just hire graduates. We hire leaders-in-waiting.

See more. Be more. Visit **barclays-graduates.co.uk/TT100** to learn more.

BARCLAYS CAPITAL

barcap.com/expectexcellence

Vacancies for around 300 graduates in 2011

- Finance
- Human Resources
- Investment Banking
- IT
- Law
- Marketing

Starting salary for 2011
£Competitive

Universities that Barclays Capital plans to visit in 2010-11

Bath, Bristol, Cambridge, Durham, Edinburgh, Glasgow, London, Loughborough, Manchester, Nottingham, Oxford, Southampton, Stirling, Strathclyde, Warwick, York
Please check with your university careers service for details of events.

Application deadline
15th November 2010

Contact Details
Turn to page 248 now to request more information or visit our new website at www.top100graduateemployers.com

Barclays Capital has more than 23,000 people in offices around the world, and has the global reach and distribution power to meet the needs of issuers and investors in all the major financial markets. Graduate and internship opportunities are offered in areas right across the firm, from Investment Banking, Sales and Trading, to Operations, IT and Human Resources.

The graduate programme is the key to the success of Barclays Capital. Senior managers across the firm are intrinsically involved in graduate training, giving graduates a remarkable degree of insight and exposure from the moment they join. The programme starts with an intensive introduction to the firm, their products, instruments and services, and the wider financial markets.

Graduates will gain more than a theoretical understanding, with a variety of case studies, workshops and presentations giving invaluable practical knowledge and skills. They can also expect comprehensive role-specific training, plus soft skills development.

As well as full-time opportunities, 10-12 week summer internships are offered and off-cycle opportunities, depending on business need. In all cases, interns will find themselves at the heart of the action. They'll gain real experience in a real role, working on anything from live transactions and marketing projects to research and analysis, depending on the business area.

As well as benefiting from extensive training before and during the programme, there are regular opportunities to network with intern colleagues, recent graduates and senior members of the firm.

EXPECT TO GO PLACES
YOU NEVER EXPECTED.

Graduate careers in investment banking

Here at Barclays Capital, we'll help you fulfil your highest ambitions in the most unexpected ways. For instance, we think the best way for you to get to the top is to learn from the people who are already there. That's why our senior managers are intrinsically involved in training our graduates – and why you can look forward to extraordinary insights and top-floor views from day one. It's time to raise your expectations. Visit our website to find out more.

barcap.com/expectexcellence

Expect Excellence

ssued by Barclays Bank PLC, authorised and regulated by the Financial Services Authority and a member of the London Stock Exchange, Barclays Capital is the investment anking division of Barclays Bank PLC, which undertakes US securities business in the name of its wholly-owned subsidiary Barclays Capital Inc., a FINRA and SIPC ember. © 2010 Barclays Bank PLC. All rights reserved. Barclays and Barclays Capital are trademarks of Barclays Bank PLC and its affiliates.

BBC

www.bbc.co.uk/jobs

Possible Vacancies in 2011

- Engineering
- Finance
- General Management
- IT
- Law
- Marketing
- Media
- Research & Development

Starting salary for 2011
£Competitive

Universities that the BBC plans to visit in 2010-11
Please check with your university careers service for details of events.

Application deadline
Year-round recruitment

Contact Details
✉ hr@bbchrdirect.co.uk
☎ 0370 333 1330

Turn to page 248 now to request more information or visit our new website at www.top100graduateemployers.com

The BBC is one of the world's best-known broadcasting brands and today's digital BBC plays a key role in modern life. As an organisation funded by the universal licence fee, the BBC's mission is to inform, educate and entertain. 97% of the UK's adult population uses BBC services each week (not to mention millions more around the globe). It is watched, listened to, read and interacted with via 8 network TV stations, 10 network radio and numerous local radio stations, its award winning website and via the Red Button too.

In this new digital, on-demand world, the BBC's role is changing from a one-way, studio-based broadcaster of programmes, into an audience focused 'anytime, anywhere, anyhow', content brand. New services, like iPlayer, are strengthening this change in direction and maintaining the BBC's place at the forefront of the broadcasting world.

This forward-thinking approach extends beyond its services. The BBC is creating an environment that's friendly, welcoming and open to change. One that's as diverse as it is fast-moving, and where challenge, development and recognition go hand-in-hand.

However, while the atmosphere is relaxed, the ethic here is very hard working and there's a real focus on development at every level. So whether graduates join through one of the variety of training schemes that the BBC advertise throughout the year or by applying for a specific vacancy, they will find the right inspiration to bring their career to life.

To find out more about working at the BBC and to search and apply for current vacancies, visit bbc.co.uk/jobs

BBC RADIO 1Xtra

BBC cymru wales

BBC RADIO 3:

BBC NEWS

BBC HD

BBC iPlayer

BBC WORLD SERVICE

B B C

BBC RADIO 4

BBC Scotland

BBC FOUR

BBC NORTHERN IRELAND

BBC RADIO 7

BBC SPORT

BBC RADIO 1

BBC one

BDO

www.bdo.co.uk/graduates

Vacancies for around 200 graduates in 2011

Accountancy

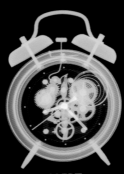

ALERT
Our clients need you to be ahead of the game

Starting salary for 2011
£Competitive
Varies regionally.

Universities that BDO plans to visit in 2010-11
Aston, Bath, Birmingham, Bristol, Cambridge, Cardiff, Durham, Exeter, Glasgow, Leeds, London, Loughborough, Manchester, Nottingham, Oxford, Southampton, Surrey, Warwick
Please check with your university careers service for details of events.

Application deadline
No official deadline
Early applications are encouraged.

Contact Details
✉ student.recruitment@bdo.co.uk
Turn to page 248 now to request more information or visit our new website at www.top100graduateemployers.com

Not all big accountancy firms are the same. BDO is building a strikingly different business, focused on exceptional client service. It employs exceptional people – and helps them get on with the job, without needless bureaucracy. Its systems work to support its people, not the other way around.

The firm is looking for graduates who don't fit the conventional accountancy mould. Talented people with the imagination and initiative to make a real difference – to be the difference that matters so much to its clients. It doesn't want clones. Its people are as diverse as its clients: individuals who can think for themselves, appreciate and respect people whoever they are, build relationships and take personal responsibility.

BDO's training is as exceptional – and individual – as the people it recruits. Most study for the ACA, but there are also routes to other professional qualifications. Training is tailored to their needs and centred on first-hand experience. That's why they get such excellent results.

The firm offers opportunities in a range of exciting areas from tax to forensic services, with the chance to take real responsibility on projects alongside partners and colleagues. Refreshingly, its partners are known for their hands-on involvement, and mutual support is an essential part of the culture. Successful applicants could also spend time abroad: BDO is a global accountancy network with more than 1,000 offices in over 100 countries.

What else? BDO has figured repeatedly in The Sunday Times and FT best places to work lists, and won a number of service and sector related awards including Accountancy Age 'Tax Team of the Year', 'Audit Team of the Year' and 'Corporate Finance Deal of the Year' to name but a few.

THE DIFFERENCE INSIDE

Graduate careers in accountancy

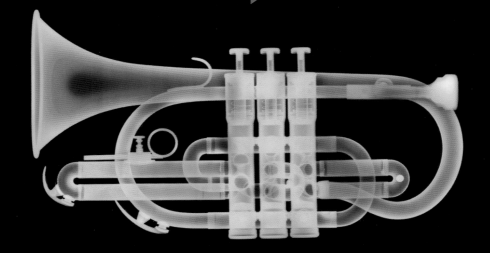

OPINION

Valued by us, important to our clients

We are different because our people are. By empowering people just like you, we're able to provide our clients with the exceptional service that makes our firm unique.

At BDO your individuality will be valued. We'll give you the training and opportunity to develop your talents and achieve your goals.

Apply online at www.bdo.co.uk/graduates

Bloomberg

careers.bloomberg.com

Vacancies for around
400+ graduates in 2011

- Finance
- IT
- Media
- Research & Development
- Sales

Starting salary for 2011
£Competitive

Universities Bloomberg plans to visit in 2010-11

Aston, Bath, Birmingham, Bristol, Cambridge, Cardiff, City, Dublin, Durham, Edinburgh, Leeds, Leicester, Liverpool, London, Manchester, Nottingham, Oxford, Sheffield, Southampton, Warwick, York
Please check with your university careers service for details of events.

Application deadline
Year-round recruitment

Contact Details
Turn to page 248 now to request more information or visit our new website at
www.top100graduateemployers.com

Bloomberg is a leading global provider of data, news and analytics. The Bloomberg Professional® Service and Bloomberg's media services provide real-time and archived financial and market data, pricing, trading, news and communications tools in a single, integrated package.

Bloomberg's clients include corporations, news organisations, financial and legal professionals, and individuals around the world. With over 11,000 employees operating in more than 153 countries, Bloomberg is truly international. The largest offices include New York, London and Tokyo, and this is where the majority of graduate opportunities are located.

Graduate positions include financial sales, software development, global data, IT, project management, news and many more. For most roles, a second language is desirable but not essential. Bloomberg recruits all year round and from any discipline. A passion for finance, technology or an international career is required. Bloomberg breaks down barriers between people and encourages communication by bringing colleagues together. With no job titles or executive areas, the culture fosters interaction at every level.

Bloomberg supports community programmes by reinvesting resources back into society through sponsorships and employee volunteer activities. But the real depth and diversity of Bloomberg's way of life comes from the creativity and commitment of its people. Training is extensive and ongoing via Bloomberg University. Courses are wide-ranging and available to all, allowing graduates to progress quickly and take on real responsibility quickly. Opportunities are listed on the website and start dates are available throughout the year.

MOVE THE MARKETS.
Innovate from the front.

Join the company at the forefront of finance and technology.

Bloomberg provides information to business leaders around the world. Our employees have a passion for excellence, no matter what their experience is. We foster that passion and encourage growth and development in every way possible.

We have opportunities in Financial Sales, Data Analysis, Software Development, News and many more areas. Bloomberg is the ideal place for you to develop your knowledge and enthusiasm for the financial markets. **Join Bloomberg.**

careers.bloomberg.com

Bloomberg is a proud Equal Opportunity Employer. ©2009 Bloomberg L.P. All rights reserved. 34839393 0609

BNP PARIBAS
CORPORATE & INVESTMENT BANKING

www.graduates.bnpparibas.com

Vacancies for around
300+ graduates in 2011

- Engineering
- Finance
- Human Resources
- Investment Banking
- IT
- Marketing

Vacancies also available in Europe,
the USA and Asia.

Starting salary for 2011
£Competitive

Universities BNP Paribas
plans to visit in 2010-11

Bath, Bristol, Cambridge,
Durham, Leeds, London,
Manchester, Nottingham,
Nottingham Trent, Oxford,
St Andrews, Warwick
Please check with your university
careers service for details of events.

Application deadline
See website for full details.

Contact Details
Turn to page 248 now to request more
information or visit our new website at
www.top100graduateemployers.com

BNP Paribas Corporate & Investment Banking is a leading
European investment bank with global leadership in many of
its businesses. The company is part of the BNP Paribas
Group, one of the six strongest banks in the world, rated AA
by Standard & Poor's, and the largest bank in the eurozone
by deposits. With over 19,000 employees in 53 countries,
BNP Paribas can offer graduates a truly global career.

The organisation's stability and culture of strong risk management underpin a
drive for quality and innovation at the service of its clients in both mature and
emerging markets, and across a diverse range of products and asset classes.
Building on a strong performance in recent challenging conditions, BNP Paribas
is now pursuing its ambitions to grow its global network and extend its client
base. With a focus on delivering intelligent, practical and above all effective
solutions for clients, it offers international career opportunities at graduate and
internship level across all areas of corporate and investment banking.

BNP Paribas is committed to early and rapid career development. Once it
has identified the best fit for its graduates' skills and ambitions they will be
hired directly into identified positions. As well as first-class formal training,
successful applicants will benefit from on-the-job coaching and support from
sector-leading professionals. In this collaborative and nurturing environment
graduates will learn quickly and rapidly to take on new responsibilities.

BNP Paribas would like to hear from graduates who are analytical and
entrepreneurial, numerate and can quickly understand complex financial
concepts, who have ideas and are ready to learn, and can speak good
business English.

When you think of ambition do you think of using your talents to rise to new heights in the fast-moving global markets? We do.

BNP Paribas Corporate & Investment Banking is an innovative provider of sophisticated financial and strategic solutions to large companies and financial institutions around the world. Creativity, entrepreneurialism and a relentless focus on our clients' goals have allowed us to grow into a leading European bank with a strong global presence. Our strong risk management and financial stability have enabled us to continue growing – and to help our clients grow – even in the most challenging of times. Now we are in a position to pursue bold strategies for expansion around the world.

We have a tradition of doing things differently here, pursuing our own ideas and working collaboratively to achieve exceptional results for our clients. If you're interested in joining an international team and launching an exciting career in the fast-moving financial markets, then find out where you could fit in at BNP Paribas.

Careers in Corporate & Investment Banking
www.graduates.bnpparibas.com

BNP PARIBAS
CORPORATE & INVESTMENT BANKING | The bank for a changing world

Vacancies for around 55 graduates in 2011

- Finance
- IT
- Marketing
- Retailing

Starting salary for 2011
c.£23,000
Plus benefits.

Universities that Boots plans to visit in 2010-11
Cambridge, Manchester, Nottingham, Warwick
Please check with your university careers service for details of events.

Application deadline
See website for full details.

Contact Details
Turn to page 248 now to request more information or visit our new website at www.top100graduateemployers.com

www.boots.jobs/graduates

Boots continues to enjoy phenomenal success as a leading UK health and beauty business. With last year's profits soaring beyond £1 billion, they're trusted by millions to deliver legendary customer care.

Maintaining that edge requires a 3,000-strong team of people who genuinely love creating 'feel-good' experiences for their customers, colleagues and the business. Graduates play an essential role in this success, and are part of Boots' new programme that aims to fast-track them as future business leaders.

In 2011, the Boots Graduate Programme will cover four business areas. The Retail Management Programme is designed to produce future store leaders, who can offer Boots' customers the experience they expect each time they walk into a store. The Brand, Buying & Marketing Programme teaches graduates how to develop, source and market Boots' brands (including No.7 and Botanics) as well as a huge range of external brands. Their award-winning Finance Programme offers hands-on experience in financial accounting, management information and business partnering. Boots will also fund the ACCA or CIMA qualification. March 2011 will also see the launch of the new IT Graduate Programme.

While a relevant business, retail or finance-related degree is ideal, it's more important that graduates bring their passion for retail and are excited by the prospect of driving the future business. In return, they can expect a great range of benefits that include bonuses, discounted health and dental plans, over 100 discounted benefits (including insurance, health club memberships and holidays), discounts on Boots products, plus a stakeholder pension and generous holidays.

"I helped plan all the media for the launch of an 'Exclusive to Boots' product. It was so exciting. We sold a million in the first fortnight."

Brand, Buying & Marketing | Retail Management | Finance | IT

"Completing Boots' graduate programme gave me a fantastic insight into the different areas of our business. From competitor analysis and buying skincare products, through to new product launches, being in the thick of such high-profile work is so exciting – and also typical of the way that Boots gets the best out of you."

Read my full story, and find out more about all our graduate programmes at
www.boots.jobs/graduates

THE SUNDAY TIMES
25
BEST BIG COMPANIES TO WORK FOR
2010

feel good

Jamie,
Assistant Buying Manager

BCG
THE BOSTON CONSULTING GROUP

www.bcg.com

Vacancies for around 30 graduates in 2011

Consulting

Starting salary for 2011
£Competitive

Universities that Boston Consulting Group plans to visit in 2010-11
Cambridge, London, Oxford
Please check with your university careers service for details of events.

Application deadline
7th November 2010

Contact Details
✉ lonrecruiting@bcg.com
☎ 020 7753 5353

Turn to page 248 now to request more information or visit our new website at www.top100graduateemployers.com

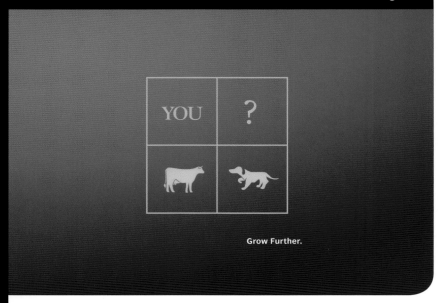

Grow Further.

The Boston Consulting Group (BCG) is a global management consulting firm and the world's leading advisor on business strategy. BCG helps their clients achieve sustainable competitive advantage, build more capable organisations and secure lasting results. BCG's customised approach combines deep insight into the dynamics of companies and markets with close collaboration at all levels in our clients' organisations.

New graduates can make a difference at BCG. They will collaborate with the world's leading businesses on a wide range of high-level strategic challenges. As part of a BCG project team, a new graduate will partner with clients to identify their highest-value opportunities, address their most critical challenges and transform their businesses. They will drive client results, helping leaders in business not just play better, but change the rules of the game.

BCG cares about personal growth. BCG's career development programme ensures consultants are mentored, stretched, and intellectually challenged. BCG's international training programme helps consultants develop a comprehensive toolkit of business and management skills. BCG employees have the opportunity to be sponsored through an MBA at a leading business school, to choose a secondment with a world-class client, and to work in one of over 60 offices around the world.

BCG is winning. Since 1990 BCG have grown at an industry-beating 16 percent annually. This growth creates expansive opportunity for BCG's people: broader choices, faster learning, and rapid advancement. Graduates with excellent analytical abilities balanced with impressive interpersonal skills, as well as drive and curiosity, can realise their potential at BCG.

Grow Further.

At BCG, your potential is limited only by your talents and ambitions. You will work daily with the world's leading businesses on a wide range of high-level strategic challenges. The knowledge, experience, and skills you'll gain will provide the springboard you need to excel in any field within BCG or beyond.

How far will you grow?

BCG

THE BOSTON CONSULTING GROUP

bp

www.bp.com/ukgraduates

Vacancies for around 120 graduates in 2011

- Accountancy
- Engineering
- Finance
- Logistics

Starting salary for 2011
£Competitive

Universities that BP plans to visit in 2010-11

Bath, Birmingham, Cambridge, Leeds, London, Manchester, Nottingham, Oxford, Strathclyde
Please check with your university careers service for details of events.

Application deadline
See website for full details.

Contact Details
☎ 0800 279 2088

Turn to page 248 now to request more information or visit our new website at www.top100graduateemployers.com

BP's business is the exploration, production, refining, marketing, trading and distribution of energy, and they do it on a phenomenal scale. They own or part-own 16 refineries around the world, operate tens of thousands of miles of pipelines and run a fleet of more than 70 ships. They produce about 4 million barrels of oil equivalent per day and own world-leading brands, such as BP, Amoco, Aral and Castrol serving millions of customers each day. And in recent years, they've made profits of over $20 billion a year.

BP aim to meet a growing global demand for energy so they're going further to discover new reserves, produce cleaner fuels and develop new energies, and they're investing in the technology and the people to do it. Every year they commit more than $1 billion to technology that is shaping the future of the industry; and every year they hire 750 graduates and interns to become the managers and technical experts of the future.

BP recruits into engineering, science and business. There are opportunities within these – from chemical engineering to geoscience, chemistry to finance, trading to drilling and completions engineering. Whichever team a graduate joins, they will find the same support and encouragement to achieve new professional heights – and beyond.

BP looks for drive, enthusiasm, ambition and the ability to think creatively and relate well to others. In addition to mobility and a relevant minimum 2:1 degree, successful applicants will possess strong influencing, analytical and technical skills. To find out more and to make an application please go to www.bp.com/ukgraduates

The Challenge

Population growth
Energy demand
Climate change

You

Passion, energy and ideas

BP

Face the world's biggest energy challenges

The world
needs you

Are you up
for the challenge?
bp.com/ukgraduates

The world faces major energy issues. With population growth rising sharply, finding the energy to fuel the world's future needs is one of the most important issues facing humanity.

If you're the kind of person that wants to make a difference; if you want to see all that you have learned put to the test; if you have the passion to find new ways to create the energy we all need, then we'd like to meet you.

official partner of the
Olympic and Paralympic Games

bp

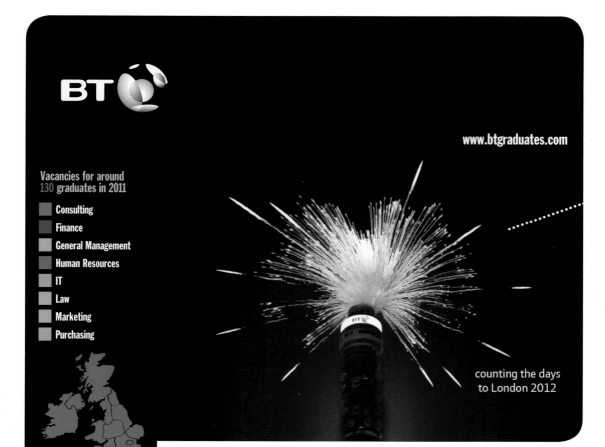

BT

www.btgraduates.com

counting the days to London 2012

Vacancies for around 130 graduates in 2011

- Consulting
- Finance
- General Management
- Human Resources
- IT
- Law
- Marketing
- Purchasing

Vacancies also available in Europe, the USA and Asia.

Starting salary for 2011
£26,500+

Universities that BT plans to visit in 2010-11

Aston, Bath, Birmingham, Bristol, Cambridge, Cardiff, Durham, Edinburgh, Essex, Exeter, Glasgow, Lancaster, Leeds, Liverpool, London, Loughborough, Manchester, Newcastle, Nottingham, Oxford, Sheffield, Southampton, St Andrews, Strathclyde, Warwick, York
Please check with your university careers service for details of events.

Application deadline
31st December 2010

Contact Details

Turn to page 248 now to request more information or visit our new website at www.top100graduateemployers.com

---

From governments to charities to multinational companies. From shops to schools to families. Every day, across the globe, BT brings people together.

But the way people stay in touch is changing, and BT is no longer just about phone calls. It is one of the world's leading providers of IT and communication services. It helps businesses become more connected, more productive and more competitive. And it helps people to communicate anywhere, at any time and with any technology they want.

BT needs fresh ideas to keep people connected and to stay ahead in the industry. And that takes more than technology – it takes people too. People who challenge, push and spot opportunities. Who ask why things are done like they are, then change them. People to work at the forefront of what BT does and to influence where it goes next.

These people can be found on BT's graduate development programme. Those that join them will get training and support to push them and make the most of their talents.

As well as learning in their role, graduates will be given plenty of opportunities for development to help them progress. And a big graduate family to support them too. They'll be encouraged to take the reins, lead their own development, and shape their own career. It'll be a steep learning curve – BT's a big company and there's lots to learn.

Welcome to the big wide world of btgraduates.com

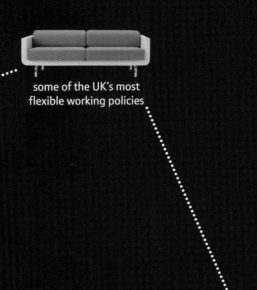

some of the UK's most
flexible working policies

reducing the number
of people driving to work

the next generation
of home entertainment

what connects?
the big wide world of btgraduates.com

a new form of
online photo storage

BT

CANCER RESEARCH UK

Vacancies for around 100+ graduates in 2011

- [ ] Accountancy
- [ ] Consulting
- [ ] Finance
- [x] General Management
- [x] Human Resources
- [ ] IT
- [x] Marketing
- [x] Purchasing
- [x] Research & Development
- [ ] Retailing

Starting salary for 2011
£Competitive

Universities that Cancer Research UK plans to visit in 2010-11
Bath, Bristol, Cambridge, Edinburgh, Leeds, London, Oxford, Warwick
Please check with your university careers service for details of events.

Application deadline
See website for full details.

Contact Details
✉ graduate@cancer.org.uk

Turn to page 248 now to request more information or visit our new website at www.top100graduateemployers.com

Cancer Research UK is the world's leading charity dedicated to cancer research. Their vision is that 'Together we will beat cancer' and their people have a passion, energy and commitment to achieving this ambitious agenda.

With an annual turnover of £498 million in 2008-2009, Cancer Research UK combines pioneering research, business expertise and marketing talent, making it a world class centre of scientific excellence and the largest fundraising charity in the UK.

Clearly, a career with Cancer Research UK offers plenty in the way of personal fulfilment. But it's also a considerable challenge, calling for excellent communication skills, strategic thinking, innovation and a determination to pursue fresh possibilities.

Every year, Cancer Research UK offers a variety of graduate opportunities in all aspects of their work, including fundraising, marketing, communications, science and corporate services. Few organisations can offer such a unique range of opportunities or allow graduates to make a real contribution. As well as graduate programmes, Cancer Research UK offers PhD studentships, internships, industrial placements and a variety of voluntary opportunities. To help successful applicants achieve their own ambitions, they will benefit from a unique combination of on-the-job learning and formal training.

Cancer Research UK offers outstanding graduates the opportunity to work towards an outstanding vision.

To find out more visit their website: graduates.cancerresearchuk.org

Together we will beat cancer

CANCER RESEARCH UK

Moore major players needed

Graduate Opportunities

Innovative. Ambitious. Focused. As a talented graduate naturally you'll have high expectations for your future. So do we.

At Cancer Research UK we've made great progress, but we're always looking to raise our game. We're looking for graduates with fresh ideas and the drive to succeed. From the moment you join us, we'll invest in your talent and give you the opportunity to work on important, challenging goals that deserve the focus of passionate graduates. We'll be looking to you to drive us forward.

If you've Moore ambition than most, get on the ball.

Visit www.graduates.cancerresearchuk.org

centrica

Vacancies for around 60+ graduates in 2011

- Engineering
- Finance
- General Management
- Human Resources
- IT
- Marketing

Star ting salary for 2011

£25,000

Plus a £2,100 starting bonus.

Universities that Centrica plans to visit in 2010-11

Aberdeen, Bath, Birmingham, Brunel, Cambridge, Durham, Edinburgh, Lancaster, London, Loughborough, Manchester, Oxford, Southampton, Strathclyde, Warwick
Please check with your university careers service for details of events.

Application deadline

See website for full details.

Contact Details

Turn to page 248 now to request more information or visit our new website at www.top100graduateemployers.com

Where could you fit in?

We source it · We generate it · We process it · We store it · We trade it · We supply it · We service it · We save it

Centrica is a top 30 FTSE 100 company with over 25 million customer relationships, a £21billion turnover and more than 34,000 employees. Sourcing, generating, processing, storing, trading, supplying, servicing and saving energy, the influence of this global company is all around.

A move towards a low carbon economy is high on Centrica's agenda, so the business is investing in innovative technologies and developing the skills of its people. Graduates who are ambitious and commercially savvy have an outstanding opportunity to be a future business leader in this diverse organisation.

A growing, integrated energy business, Centrica is the parent company for a range of global brands: British Gas and Direct Energy supply power and related services in the UK and US respectively; Centrica Energy manages power generation and gas production operations to ensure day-to-day customer demand is met, and Centrica Storage operates facilities that represent over 70% of the UK's total storage capacity.

The graduate programme has been designed to offer a broad grounding in the business. It offers graduates who are up for big challenges the opportunity to get involved in areas ranging from exploration and production to front-line customer service – as well as support and reward in equal measure.

Graduates will need a 2:2 or above in any discipline for all of Centrica's programmes except Engineering where they're looking for a related degree at the same level. For their highly specialised Geoscience programme, graduates will need a related MSc on top of the above.

Find out what other graduates have to say at www.centrica.com/GraduatesTT

Graduate & Summer Placement
Opportunities

We source it

We generate it

We process it

We store it

Where could you fit in?

We trade it

We supply it

We service it

We save it

Centrica is the UK's leading energy supplier and one of the greenest – sourcing, generating, processing, storing, trading, supplying, servicing and saving energy for some 25 million customer relationships.

Help us shape the future of energy and we'll help you to flourish. Graduate opportunities exist in **Customer Operations, Marketing, Human Resources, Analyst, Information Systems, Finance, Engineering and Geoscience.** We also run a 10-week **Summer Placement Programme**.

Find out more by visiting our website or using the QR code opposite. Don't know what this is? Search for QR codes online, install the reader on your mobile and scan to visit our website.

www.centrica.com/GraduatesTT

centrica

www.oncampus.citi.com

Vacancies for around 250 graduates in 2011

- Finance
- Human Resources
- Investment Banking
- IT

Starting salary for 2011
£Competitive

Universities that Citi plans to visit in 2010-11
Bath, Belfast, Bristol, Cambridge, Edinburgh, Glasgow, London, Manchester, Oxford, St Andrews, Ulster, Warwick
Please check with your university careers service for details of events.

Application deadline
7th November 2010

Contact Details
✉ campus.queries@citi.com
Turn to page 248 now to request more information or visit our new website at www.top100graduateemployers.com

Dreams.   Realities.

Citi, the leading global financial services company, has approximately 200 million customer accounts and does business in more than 140 countries.

Citi's global presence isn't just a question of size, it's a way of thinking. The organisation is passionate about what it does and is looking for graduates who want to be a part of that vision. Wherever Citi operates, it anticipates change and turns opportunities into reality. The business isn't static and neither are its people. Citi needs exceptional individuals, which is why it provides the brightest and best with an opportunity to make a difference, and ultimately a compelling career path.

Citi's 200-year heritage is built on a proud pioneering spirit, and it continues that forward-thinking tradition today. Driven by a desire for entrepreneurship and creativity, Citi is helping to shape the future of banking. It is not progress at any price, however, as it strongly believes in a commitment to responsible growth that benefits clients, colleagues and communities alike.

Citi is a lead player in its industry and a great place to start a career. Full-time and internship opportunities exist across a broad set of businesses including Investment Banking, Capital Markets Origination, Sales & Trading, Global Transaction Services, Private Bank, Risk Management, Human Resources, Operations and Technology.

Graduates with high levels of energy, enthusiasm and commitment, can help Citi to drive positive change across the organisation, the banking industry and beyond.

At Citi graduates won't just achieve their ambitions – they'll exceed them.

OPPORTUNITY NEVER SLEEPS.

Dreams. | **Realities.**

In Paris, after a hard day studying, Jen's finally ready to rest. Six time zones away, in New York, Lisa - Jen's future mentor - is shaking hands on funding for an irrigation project in Western Africa. Meanwhile, half a world away, Investment Banking Associate Rajid is returning from a meeting with government officials in Kazakhstan.

At any moment, someone in our global firm is opening new markets. Someone's closing deals. Someone's gaining skills to pass on to the next generation. A career with us is full of variety and challenge. Because Jen isn't working for us yet, but we've already been working for her. That's why, at Citi, opportunity never sleeps.
oncampus.citi.com

Opportunities in: Investment Banking, Capital Markets Origination, Sales & Trading, Global Transaction Services, Private Bank, Human Resources, Operations & Technology.

Citi never sleeps™

Application deadlines:
Full Time Analyst Programme 7th November 2010
Summer Analyst Programme 2nd January 2011

©2010 Citibank, N.A. All rights reserved. Authorized and regulated by the Financial Services Authority. Citi and Arc Design is a trademark and service mark of Citigroup Inc., used and registered throughout the world. Citi, Citi Never Sleeps, and Arc Design are service marks of Citigroup or Citibank, N.A. Citi is an equal opportunities employer.

CIVILSERVICE
FASTSTREAM

www.hmg.gov.uk/faststream

**Vacancies for around
500 graduates in 2011**

Engineering

General Management

Human Resources

IT

Starting salary for 2011
Up to £27,000

**Universities that the
Fast Stream
plans to visit in 2010-11**
Please check with your university
careers service for details of events.

Application deadline
30th November 2010

Contact Details

✉ faststream@parity.net

☎ 01276 400333

Turn to page 248 now to request more
information or visit our new website at
www.top100graduateemployers.com

The Civil Service's graduate talent management programme

Education. Health. Justice. Employment. Defence. Transport. Climate change. International development and Foreign affairs. These are just some of the areas where graduates on the Civil Service Fast Stream get to put their ideas into practice, as they work on issues that affect the entire country and beyond.

The Civil Service Fast Stream is a talent management programme aimed at people who have the potential to become the Civil Service leaders of tomorrow. As such, Fast Streamers are given considerable early responsibility from the outset, they are stretched and challenged on a daily basis, and they move regularly between projects to gain a wide range of experiences and skills.

They are exposed to three distinct but complementary professional areas: operational delivery, policy delivery and corporate services. These areas give them a wide understanding of how government delivers public services. A comprehensive training and development programme is provided to support achievement of the Fast Streamer role.

So what qualities are needed to make it to the top? Initiative, confidence, innovation, orally articulate, strong drafting skills, leadership and decisiveness are all important, as is an analytical and open-minded approach. Graduates must have a minimum 2:2 in any discipline.

Above all, they need to be the kind of people who can develop relationships and deliver results, and who are excited by the idea of making a positive and highly visible impact across many different areas of society.

There are many opportunities available, including schemes for those who want to work in parliament, the European Union, in diplomacy as well as in core Civil Service departments.

where will your IDEAS end up?

Our graduates don't just think about the big issues. They come up with innovative solutions and apply them to the real world. Employment? The economy? Climate change? Just some of the areas you could have an impact on as part of the Civil Service Fast Stream Graduate Programme. Find out more at www.hmg.gov.uk/faststream

CIVIL SERVICE FAST STREAM

CLIFFORD CHANCE

www.cliffordchance.com/gradsuk

Vacancies for around 120 graduates in 2011

For training contracts starting in 2013

 Law

Vacancies also available in Europe, the USA, Asia and elsewhere in the world.

Starting salary for 2011
£38,000

Universities that Clifford Chance plans to visit in 2010-11

Aberdeen, Bristol, Cambridge, Dundee, Durham, Edinburgh, Exeter, Glasgow, London, Manchester, Nottingham, Oxford, St Andrews, Strathclyde, Warwick, York

Please check with your university careers service for details of events.

Application deadline
Law: 31st July 2011
Non-Law: 31st Jan. 2011

Contact Details
✉ Recruitment.London
@CliffordChance.com
☎ 020 7006 3003

Turn to page 248 now to request more information or visit our new website at www.top100graduateemployers.com

At Clifford Chance, the goal is to be at the forefront of the elite group of international law firms that is emerging. Joining the firm means sharing its ambitions and developing potential as part of an exceptionally talented legal team.

Clifford Chance's practice is broad and far reaching, engaging with the issues and decisions that underpin its clients' success. Clifford Chance advises its clients internationally and domestically; under common law and civil law systems; in local and cross-border transactions and disputes; on day-to-day operations and on 'game-changing' transformational deals and issues.

Setting the pace in the legal sector, Clifford Chance has more tier-one international practices than any other law firm (Chambers Global 2010). The business is organised into six global practices – Corporate, Capital Markets, Banking and Finance, Real Estate, Litigation and Dispute resolution, and Tax, Pensions and Employment. Clifford Chance trainees will work in at least three of these practices, learning from professionals at the leading edge of the profession.

Clifford Chance is a firm of exceptional lawyers drawn from a wide range of backgrounds – there is no one 'type' here. The firm ask a lot of its trainees – focus and dedication are taken as read, but they will also need to be flexible and willing to adapt to new challenges and a lot of responsibility. Counterbalancing this is a level of investment in their career development which is only offered by a handful of professional services firms.

The Clifford Chance training programme will give successful applicants the skills and experience to begin contributing to their team immediately and to lay the foundations for a long-term, rewarding legal career.

Joining us as a trainee or a vacation scheme student means sharing our ambition and drive to set the pace in the emerging group of elite global law firms. You'll be focused on developing your potential as part of an exceptionally talented legal team and tackling the issues and decisions that shape our clients' success – helping them to achieve competitive advantage in challenging business circumstances.

Find out about opportunities at Clifford Chance – a law firm built on and recognised for collaboration, innovation and a relentless commitment to quality, with more leading cross-border practices than any other firm *(Chambers Global 2010)*.

Together we are Clifford Chance.
www.cliffordchance.com/gradsuk

We have a global commitment to diversity, dignity and inclusiveness.

Clifford Chance LLP

C L I F F O R D
C H A N C E

RANKED IN
CHAMBERS
GLOBAL
2010

The co-operative

www.co-operative.jobs/graduates

Vacancies for around 19 graduates in 2011

- Finance
- General Management

The co-operative
From community projects to a share of the profits, renewable energy to Fairtrade products, we believe that when the benefits are passed around, it's **good for everyone**

Starting salary for 2011
£Competitive

Universities that The Co-operative Group plans to visit in 2010-11
Cambridge, Lancaster, Leeds, Leicester, Manchester, Nottingham, Oxford, Sheffield
Please check with your university careers service for details of events.

Application deadline
See website for full details.

Contact Details
✉ graduate.recruitment @co-operative.coop
Turn to page 248 now to request more information or visit our new website at www.top100graduateemployers.com

With 15 different businesses, 4,900 outlets and 110,000 people, The Co-operative Group isn't just a food retailer but also a travel provider, a funeral director, a pharmacist, a legal services provider, and much more.

But the real difference lies not just in what they do; it's what they are – a co-operative (and the world's largest consumer co-operative at that). Unlike a plc, they do not just exist to make profit. Everything they do is for the benefit of their members and the community as a whole. They are driven by their social goals and their co-operative values give them a positive advantage.

But that doesn't mean they are any less ambitious – they still offer the depth and breadth of challenge expected from a commercially focussed business. For those who want to pursue a rewarding career without compromising their values, the Group offers two programmes: Business Management and Finance.

On the Business Management programme, whether it be Funeralcare, marketing or Food Retail operations, graduates can choose from a wide range of business critical projects ensuring the entire experience meets their career aspirations. On the other hand, graduates with a passion for finance might want to consider the CIMA accredited programme. This gives them transactional experience of accounting software packages and an overview of financial processes. It will sharpen their commercial approach through working directly with the different businesses, as well as giving them a broad perspective of financial strategy.

Whichever route they choose, graduates will gain experience across the businesses and develop technical knowledge and professional skills through The Co-operative Group's structured development programme.

The **co-operative**
good for everyone

Tackle the challenges facing business and the wider world

The Co-operative is one of the largest and fastest growing retailers in the UK. Yes, we are commercially focused, but we're also ethically guided. We source 99% of our energy from renewables and we always put people before profit. Here you'll be able to lead major projects in a variety of business areas, from food to travel, from marketing to operations. Whether you choose the Business Management or CIMA accredited Finance programme, you'll get close to our leaders and see strategy through to delivery. There is no other graduate programme like this and no other business like ours. We're the big business you can believe in. www.co-operative.jobs/graduates

CREDIT SUISSE

www.credit-suisse.com/careers

**Vacancies for around
250 graduates in 2011**

■ Finance
■ Investment Banking
■ IT

Vacancies also available in Europe.

Starting salary for 2011
£Competitive

**Universities Credit Suisse
plans to visit in 2010-11**
Birmingham, Cambridge,
City, Dublin,
Edinburgh, London,
Manchester, Oxford,
Southampton, Warwick
Please check with your university
careers service for details of events.

Application deadline
Year-round recruitment

Contact Details
Turn to page 248 now to request more
information or visit our new website at
www.top100graduateemployers.com

Credit Suisse is one of the world leaders in global financial services, providing private banking, investment banking and asset management services to clients around the world. It is active in over fifty countries, with a team of 47,000 people. Credit Suisse offers advisory services and comprehensive solutions to companies, institutions and high-net-worth individuals worldwide. Its vision is to be the world's most admired bank.

Credit Suisse offers challenging professional opportunities, exceptional rewards and global development potential for people who are prepared to look at the world in a different way. There are opportunities in private banking, investment banking (including fixed income and equities), asset management, information technology, operations and other support functions.

Many people who join Credit Suisse do so because of their strong culture. Credit Suisse appeals to intelligent and outgoing personalities who want to work in an atmosphere of co-operation and respect.

The organisation needs individuals who bring something personal, special and unique to the business. The creativity, flair and agility that makes Credit Suisse successful flows directly from the special mix of people who work here.

Delivered by Credit Suisse's award winning Business School, the training programmes are designed to be best in class. Content varies among business areas, but all programmes combine formal learning with on-the-job practice and personal coaching to create an environment for further development. Continual learning and growth is always encouraged at Credit Suisse.

5 points of view
1,000 opinions
One Credit Suisse
investing in your future

There's great strength in keeping an open mind and great wisdom to be had from sharing personal experiences. We encourage our people to collaborate and share their knowledge, to really understand our clients needs and to deliver excellence consistently. This enables us to drive our business forward and helps our clients thrive.

Take a closer look at **credit-suisse.com/careers**

This advertisement has been approved solely for the purposes of Section 21 of the Financial Services and Markets Act 2000 by Credit Suisse Securities (Europe) Limited of One Cabot Square, London E14 4QJ. Credit Suisse is an Equal Opportunity Employer and does not discriminate in its employment decisions on the basis of any protected category. © 2010 CREDIT SUISSE GROUP AG and/or its affiliates. All rights reserved.

Deloitte.

**Vacancies for around
1,000 graduates in 2011**

- Accountancy
- Consulting
- Finance
- IT

Starting salary for 2011
£Competitive

**Universities that Deloitte
plans to visit in 2010-11**
Aberdeen, Aston, Bath,
Birmingham, Bristol,
Cambridge, Cardiff, Dublin,
Durham, Edinburgh, Exeter,
Glasgow, Heriot-Watt,
Lancaster, Leeds, Leicester,
Liverpool, London,
Loughborough, Manchester,
Newcastle, Nottingham,
Oxford, Reading, Sheffield,
Southampton, St Andrews,
Strathclyde, Surrey, Sussex,
Ulster, Warwick, York
Please check with your university
careers service for details of events.

Application deadline
Year-round recruitment

Contact Details
Turn to page 248 now to request more
information or visit our new website at
www.top100graduateemployers.com

It's your future
How far will you take it?

www.deloitte.co.uk/graduates

What can Deloitte offer graduates that no one else can?
Discover more about Deloitte and find out.

Deloitte rely on talented graduates. With their freshness, insight and
innovative thinking, they can help them realise their goal to be the most
trusted professional services firm in the world.

Deloitte already lead the way, providing Audit, Tax, Consulting and Corporate
Finance services across all major industries. Graduates can work with clients
in financial services, technology, media & telecommunications, consumer
business or travel.

Whatever the degree subject and whichever service line is chosen,
in joining Deloitte graduates could be working with clients in all these areas.
It's this breadth of experience that offers graduates the complexity and
challenges they yearn for. This is why graduates can grow further and faster
at Deloitte than perhaps anywhere else, and why they can provide them with
a career that will stimulate, reward and motivate like no other.

Deloitte can't promise an easy ride, but what they can promise is real
responsibility early on, the chance to learn from some of the foremost
experts in their field, all the support graduates will need to obtain professional
qualifications and a real commitment to developing organisational and
leadership qualities.

With all these opportunities, it's down to graduates to make the most
of them.

To find out more about Deloitte – and the 1,000 roles they have for talented
graduates and undergraduates – visit www.deloitte.co.uk/graduates

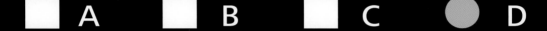

Make the right choice

Choose from our range of graduate and undergraduate opportunities in Audit, Tax, Consulting or Corporate Finance to start something special. If you're interested in joining a world-leading professional services firm that will challenge, develop and reward you in equal measure, visit www.deloitte.co.uk/graduates to see what your options are. It's your future. How far will you take it?

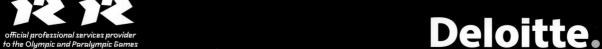

official professional services provider
to the Olympic and Paralympic Games

Deloitte.

© 2010 Deloitte LLP. Deloitte LLP is an equal opportunities employer.

DIAGEO

www.diageo.com/careers

Vacancies for around 100 graduates in 2011

- Engineering
- Finance
- Human Resources
- Logistics
- Marketing
- Purchasing
- Sales

Vacancies also available in Europe.

Starting salary for 2011
£Competitive

Universities that Diageo plans to visit in 2010-11
Aston, Birmingham, Bristol, Cambridge, Dublin, London, Manchester, Nottingham, Oxford, Warwick
Please check with your university careers service for details of events.

Application deadline
Year-round recruitment

Contact Details
✉ globalcareers@diageo.com
Turn to page 248 now to request more information or visit our new website at www.top100graduateemployers.com

While they may not know the company, people everywhere have heard of the brands. Because Guinness, Smirnoff, Pimms and Tanqueray are among the world's most loved. And graduates who'd relish the chance to join the team behind them all should get in touch with…guess who?

Diageo. The world's leading premium drinks company. Diageo employs over 23,000 people in around 180 markets. All with one aim: to help millions of people celebrate life every day, everywhere.

Diageo celebrates success. Through close collaboration and true team spirit, the company prides itself on achieving things that others may consider unachievable. They also promote a happy work/life balance. No wonder they're among the world's most admired companies to work for.

Being a truly global company, Diageo's structured, three-year training programme often gives opportunities to work in different parts of the world. Successful applicants will be bright, passionate graduates. Some will have a creative flair for marketing or a talent for sales. Others will find their niche in Supply Chain, HR, or Finance. All roles provide real challenges from day one – preparing graduates to become future leaders of the business, with support from a dedicated buddy and mentor.

The company looks for people who are authentic in what they do; people who can demonstrate high levels of integrity. An ability to generate new ideas and bring them to life is essential.

As expected, Diageo offers a competitive salary and great benefits to help their graduates live life to the full.

Guinness, José Cuervo, Pimm's, Baileys, Johnnie Walker, Smirnoff,… how long did it take you
to recognise our brands? Probably not that long. After all, they're some of the best known in
the world. The real question, though, is do you know the name behind them all? The answer
is Diageo. We're the world's leading premium drinks company – and we're looking for bright
graduates who'd like the chance to work on some of the world's most loved brands.
Sounds like you? Discover more at **www.diageo.com/careers**

DIAGEO

drinkaware.co.uk for the facts about alcohol

**Vacancies for around
85 graduates in 2011**
For training contracts starting in 2013

 Law

Starting salary for 2011
£Competitive

**Universities DLA Piper
plans to visit in 2010-11**
Aberdeen, Belfast,
Birmingham, Bristol,
Cambridge, Dundee,
Durham, Edinburgh,
Exeter, Glasgow, Kent,
Leeds, Leicester, Liverpool,
London, Manchester,
Newcastle, Nottingham,
Oxford, Sheffield,
Strathclyde, Warwick, York
Please check with your university
careers service for details of events.

Application deadline
31st July 2011

Contact Details
recruitment.graduate
@dlapiper.com
Turn to page 248 now to request more
information or visit our new website at
www.top100graduateemployers.com

DLA Piper is one of the world's largest law firms. With more
than 3,500 lawyers across 30 countries throughout Asia,
Europe, the Middle East and the US, DLA Piper is positioned to
help companies with their legal needs anywhere in the world.

Their current vision is to be the leading global business law firm.
Clients include some of the world's leading businesses, governments,
banks and financial institutions. DLA Piper offers trainees in all UK offices
the opportunity to apply for a range of client and international secondments.

In 2008 DLA Piper won the prestigious National Graduate Recruitment Awards'
'Diversity Recruitment Award' proving their commitment to recruiting people
from a wide variety of backgrounds and ages.

There is no 'standard' DLA Piper trainee, however they do require a strong
academic background and look for good communicators and team players.
As well as this, in line with the firm's main focus of work, a keen interest in
the corporate world is essential – as is an appetite for life!

Trainees complete four six-month seats and progress is monitored
through regular reviews and feedback. The in-house Professional
Skills Course combined with high-quality on-the-job experience means
an excellent grounding on which DLA Piper's trainees build their
professional careers.

The firm operates a formal summer scheme, which runs between June
and August each year. The schemes run for two weeks and allow a
thorough insight into DLA Piper. There are approximately 170 places
available nationwide.

SQUEEZE MORE INTO TWO YEARS
WE OFFER YOU ONE OF THE SHARPEST TRAINING CONTRACTS AROUND

Everything matters and every day counts when you're a trainee at DLA Piper. We squeeze huge amounts of experience, responsibility and personal development into your 24 months with us. That means you get to know more about the law, our firm and about yourself.

Working with one of the world's leading practices also means more opportunities: the chance to try the things you want to try, work on secondments abroad or with clients, and get involved with headline making matters.

Enjoy every last bit of your training contract and develop the all round skills that all top lawyers need. Visit our website for more details: www.dlapipergraduates.co.uk or follow us on Facebook.

www.dlapiper.com | DLA Piper UK LLP

EVERYTHING MATTERS

DLA Piper is an international legal practice, the members of which are separate and distinct legal entities.
For further information please refer to www.dlapiper.com/structure.

e·on

www.eon-uk.com/graduates

Vacancies for around 40 graduates in 2011

- Engineering
- Finance
- General Management
- Human Resources
- IT
- Marketing
- Sales

Vacancies also available in Europe.

Starting salary for 2011
£25,267

Universities that E.ON plans to visit in 2010-11

Aston, Birmingham, Bristol, Brunel, Cambridge, Cardiff, Edinburgh, Lancaster, London, Loughborough, Nottingham, Nottingham Trent, Sheffield, Southampton, Surrey, Warwick
Please check with your university careers service for details of events.

Application deadline
See website for full details.

Contact Details

✉ gradrecruitment@eon-uk.com

Turn to page 248 now to request more information or visit our new website at www.top100graduateemployers.com

As one of the world's largest investor owned energy companies, the decisions that E.ON makes matter. Using its size and resources to tackle climate change head-on, finding a way to produce clean, reliable and affordable energy, building a future infrastructure the world can be proud of; these are just some of the challenges E.ON faces. By joining E.ON, graduates can play a leading role in rising to them.

E.ON's graduate programmes in Engineering, International Business Management, Finance, Human Resources, Commercial Management and IT are designed to stretch and challenge. They'll expose graduates to all areas of E.ON's international business and give them lots of responsibility. In return for dedication, courage and initiative, graduates will be rewarded with a great starting salary, lots of benefits and the chance to build an international career.

E.ON ensures successful graduates receive the right training to rise to new challenges. Each individual is assigned a mentor who will support them from day one and help with their personal development plans (including the opportunity to gain professional qualifications). They will also join part of the E.ON graduate network to share information and experiences and listen to different points of view.

E.ON is investing billions in developing a diverse generation portfolio over the coming years, using the latest technologies to reduce carbon emissions and improve energy efficiency. So, from tackling large scale projects to gaining professional qualifications, all those who demonstrate passion, commitment and drive will have the chance to become E.ON's future technical or business leaders – making a positive impact on people's lives and the environment.

On your future

It's by working together that we get things done, and rise to new challenges. Just ask our graduates. Working with mentors, each other and the rest of our business, they're gaining the skills and professional qualifications they need to tackle the energy industry's greatest challenges head-on. Like how we'll go about meeting tomorrow's energy demands in a sustainable way. Or how changes in technology will affect the way we do everything – from growing our team to selling our products at an affordable price. These aren't just questions for engineers. Whatever your discipline, you could find your place here, and make your mark on the energy landscape.

To see how your energy could shape the future, visit
eon-uk.com/graduates

Save today. Save tomorrow.

eDF
ENERGY

www.edfenergy.com/TT100

**Vacancies for around
100 graduates in 2011**

- Engineering
- Finance
- General Management
- Human Resources
- Other

Vacancies also available in Europe.

Starting salary for 2011
£25,000

**Universities EDF Energy
plans to visit in 2010-11**

Bath, Birmingham,
Cambridge, Cardiff,
London, Manchester,
Oxford, Sheffield,
Strathclyde, Warwick
Please check with your university
careers service for details of events.

Application deadline
December 2010

Contact Details
✉ graduateenquiries@
edfenergy.com

Turn to page 248 now to request more
information or visit our new website at
www.top100graduateemployers.com

In the coming years, the energy industry will face some of the greatest challenges in its history. Fluctuating oil prices, fierce competition, the need for investment, the growing challenge posed by climate change – all of these will play a part.

EDF Energy is perfectly placed to tackle these issues – because it is growing too. In 2009, EDF Energy joined forces with British Energy to become the largest generator of low carbon electricity in the UK, and a major player in nuclear power.

The integration of the two companies makes EDF Energy a unique proposition. They boast expertise in a wide range of energy sources – and across every stage of the energy process: generation, trading, distribution and supply. They're championing sustainability through partnerships with the Mayor of London and London 2012. They're also involved in major projects – from airports to business districts. In fact, with British Energy on board, they're likely to be directly involved with the major developments of the industry for many years to come.

The same can be said for their graduates: the schemes are designed to support, test and develop people who have the potential to be future industry leaders. As one might expect from such an extraordinarily diverse organisation, there are a number of areas graduates can explore. Within the Networks, Existing Nuclear and New Nuclear business units, there are opportunities in civil, electrical, mechanical and chemical engineering; physics, chemistry and mathematics; and a wide range of business areas – from finance and commercial to analysis.

It takes many brilliant minds to tackle the world's energy challenges.

Which is why we're looking to add more.

www.edfenergy.com/TT100

Save today. Save tomorrow.

☰ ERNST & YOUNG

Quality In Everything We Do

www.ey.com/uk/careers

**Vacancies for around
650 graduates in 2011**

- Accountancy
- Consulting
- Finance
- IT

**Starting salary for 2011
£Competitive**

**Universities that
Ernst & Young
plans to visit in 2010-11**

Aberdeen, Aston, Bath,
Birmingham, Bristol,
Cambridge, Cardiff, City,
Durham, Edinburgh, Exeter,
Glasgow, Heriot-Watt, Hull,
Lancaster, Leeds, Liverpool,
Loughborough, Manchester,
Newcastle, Nottingham,
Oxford, Reading, Sheffield,
Southampton, St Andrews,
Strathclyde, Surrey,
Warwick, York
**Please check with your university
careers service for details of events.**

**Application deadline
Year-round recruitment**

Contact Details

✉ gradrec@uk.ey.com

Turn to page 248 now to request more
information or visit our new website at
www.top100graduateemployers.com

Go from strength to strength

Ernst & Young is interested in graduates' individual strengths and abilities, not just what they're studying. That's because the things that make them good at what they do are the same things that make them successful at work. So working out what their talents are and making the most of them will help them go further, faster, and they'll have a more enjoyable time getting there.

Ernst & Young is 144,000 people, in 700 locations across 140 countries around the world, and helps clients realise the potential in their business through Assurance, Corporate Finance, Tax and Advisory services. Ernst & Young works with some of the biggest and best-known names in business and industry, and anticipating and meeting their needs is the firm's top priority. It takes ingenuity, creativity and hard work, and the business thrives on the diversity of its people and their different abilities. With 87 practices in Europe, the Middle East, India and Africa now operating as a single EMEIA area, graduates get the opportunity to work in borderless and expert teams.

Ernst & Young will give successful applicants comprehensive training, a dedicated counsellor and a senior mentor – and if they are studying for a professional qualification they'll receive all the support they need to succeed. The scale and scope of the organisation means a broad range of careers are available – but the direction and drive will need to come from its graduates.

Graduate and internship vacancies are available now across the UK. Find out more at www.ey.com/uk/careers

Go from strength to strength

Whether you're a quick thinker, a good talker or a creative spark, it's your individual strengths we're interested in, not just what you're studying.

People who do what they're naturally good at in their careers go further, faster, and have a more enjoyable time getting there.

If you want to go from strength to strength, working in a team that helps our clients solve some of the most interesting challenges in business, then get in touch.

We have graduate and undergraduate opportunities available now in Assurance, Tax, Corporate Finance and Advisory.

Find out more at www.ey.com/uk/careers

ERNST & YOUNG
Quality In Everything We Do

INVESTORS IN PEOPLE

Stonewall
DIVERSITY CHAMPION

© Ernst & Young 2010. Ernst & Young is an equal opportunities employer and welcomes applications from all sections of the community. The UK firm Ernst & Young LLP is a limited liability partnership and a member firm of Ernst & Young Global Limited.

ExxonMobil

www.exxonmobil.com/ukrecruitment

Vacancies for around 30 graduates in 2011

- Engineering
- Finance
- IT
- Marketing
- Retailing
- Sales

Vacancies also available elsewhere in the world.

Starting salary for 2011
£33,500+

Universities ExxonMobil plans to visit in 2010-11

Aberdeen, Aston, Bath, Belfast, Birmingham, Cambridge, Edinburgh, Heriot-Watt, London, Loughborough, Manchester, Newcastle, Nottingham, Southampton, Strathclyde, Surrey
Please check with your university careers service for details of events.

Application deadline
Year-round recruitment

Contact Details

✉ uk.vacancies@exxonmobil.com

Turn to page 248 now to request more information or visit our new website at www.top100graduateemployers.com

ExxonMobil is the world's largest publicly traded international oil and gas company, providing energy that helps underpin growing economies and improve living standards around the world. It operates facilities or market products in most of the world's countries and explore for oil and natural gas on six continents.

In the UK – where the organisation is best known by its familiar brand names, Esso and Mobil – ExxonMobil has both global and local customers, ranging from major airlines to the million motorists a day who visit their service stations.

Graduates progress through specific operational roles, to gain a broad range of experiences throughout their career with the company. Rapid skills growth and career development is standard and graduates can expect a high degree of intellectual challenge and change throughout their career. A broad range of exciting opportunities are available within both commercial and technical functions, where graduates can expect immediate responsibility. Job rotations offer graduates the opportunity to test and develop their skills, applying them to new and exciting challenges.

ExxonMobil offers various development programmes, aimed at equipping graduates with the skills required to become leaders of the future. Graduates will experience early career training and development via functional programmes designed to develop technical or commercial skills. Graduates will also receive personal skills training tailored to their individual needs. Obtaining Chartership status is also encouraged where appropriate, e.g. IChemE and CIMA.

By 2030, global energy demand will increase by about 35%.

It's a **challenge** like no other.
And it will be solved by someone like **you**.

Commercial Opportunities
Gas & Power Marketing
Finance
Geoscience
Information Technology
Production
Refining & Chemicals
One Year placements
Summer placements
Graduate positions

The need for energy is a very real economic issue. It affects literally everyone – everywhere in the world. At ExxonMobil, we're uniquely positioned to help find the answers to the world's toughest energy challenges. We have the resources, the technology, and the commitment of people just like you.

When you build your career here, you have the opportunity to make a profound impact. From inventing new technologies, to unlocking new sources of petroleum, to developing more efficient fuel and engine systems, you can make the breakthroughs happen.

The biggest challenges attract the best. Whether your background is in business, engineering or science, ExxonMobil has a challenging career waiting for you.

exxonmobil.com/ukrecruitment

Esso **Mobil**

Brands of **ExxonMobil**

ExxonMobil

Taking on the world's toughest energy challenges.™

FRESHFIELDS BRUCKHAUS DERINGER

www.freshfields.com/uktrainees

Vacancies for around 90 graduates in 2011
For training contracts starting in 2013

■ Law

Starting salary for 2011
£39,000

Universities Freshfields Bruckhaus Deringer plans to visit in 2010-11
Bath, Birmingham, Bristol, Cambridge, Cardiff, City, Dublin, Durham, Edinburgh, Exeter, Glasgow, Leeds, Leicester, Liverpool, London, Manchester, Newcastle, Nottingham, Oxford, Sheffield, Southampton, St Andrews, Warwick, York
Please check with your university careers service for details of events.

Application deadline
31st July 2011

Contact Details
✉ uktrainees@freshfields.com
☎ 020 7785 5554
Turn to page 248 now to request more information or visit our new website at www.top100graduateemployers.com

Freshfields Bruckhaus Deringer is one of a handful of leading international law firms. The firm's clients are mainly big commercial businesses whose names are well-known. The type of work it does divides into helping clients achieve what they want through doing deals, advising them on real and potential problems, and helping them sort out their disputes.

Whatever clients want to achieve, their lawyers' job is to find out whether and how they can do it. Is it possible? What will be the most effective structure? What are the risks? How should it be documented?

The firm wants its trainees to come from diverse backgrounds; and their choice of university or degree is immaterial. Current trainees studied at nearly 50 different universities. Many did a law degree, but others read subjects ranging from music to biochemistry.

Whatever their background, trainees need some non-negotiable qualities. They need to be intellectually talented and have excellent English skills. They need to enjoy working on difficult problems, working alongside others, and never doing less than the best they can.

Trainees can move departments every three months, so they can see more of what's on offer. Other firms are not so flexible.

All departments provide formal training. But trainees learn most by working for clients alongside the firm's more experienced lawyers. They learn in London and in other offices in the US, Europe and Asia. Some are also seconded to clients. Every piece of research or drafting is an opportunity to learn more.

FRESHFIELDS BRUCKHAUS DERINGER

2461 great lawyers. Room for 90 more.
What you read is what you'll get. Why us?
Once you meet us you'll just know.
And we'll know too.

To find out more, go to
www.freshfields.com/uktrainees

REAL GRADUATES
AMAZING LAWYERS
STRETCHED MINDS
FANTASTIC CLIENTS
GRACE UNDER PRESSURE
EXCEPTIONAL TRAINING
UNEXCEPTIONAL BISCUITS
WORK LIKE CRAZY
LOYAL FRIENDS
DETERMINED
CHARMING PARTNERS
INTERNATIONAL DEALS
CONSCIENTIOUS
LATE FOR DINNER (AGAIN...)
SHARED ACHIEVEMENTS
OCCASIONAL GLORY

provider
Olympic and
Paralympic Games

www.careersinbritishintelligence.co.uk

**Vacancies for around
75 graduates in 2011**

■ **Engineering**
■ **IT**
■ **Research & Development**
□ **Other**

Starting salary for 2011
c.£25,000

**Universities that GCHQ
plans to visit in 2010-11**
Please check with your university
careers service for details of events.

Application deadline
Varies by function
See website for full details.

Contact Details
✉ recruitment@gchq.gsi.gov.uk

Turn to page 248 now to request more
information or visit our new website at
www.top100graduateemployers.com

GCHQ – the Government Communications Headquarters –
is one of the UK's three intelligence and security agencies
(alongside MI5 and MI6). The only one based outside London
– in Cheltenham, Gloucestershire – it plays a crucial role
in countering threats to British people and interests.

GCHQ has two specific functions. The first is Signals Intelligence — using some
of the world's most powerful technology to gather and analyse intelligence to
help shape Britain's response to global events. Teams of IT, electronics and
telecommunications specialists manage the equipment, while mathematicians,
linguists and intelligence analysts study and interpret the information
it provides. This information is then used by GCHQ's customers — for example,
the Government, law enforcement agencies and the military — to inform foreign
policy or fight terrorism and crime.

GCHQ's second function is Information Assurance – working to protect and
secure information on Government IT and communication systems from hackers
and other threats. This work is carried out by CESG – the National Technical
Authority for Information Assurance.

The focus is on keeping one step ahead of people who are, in turn, trying to
keep one step ahead of GCHQ. This means the work is constantly evolving,
extremely challenging, and always interesting. GCHQ employs around 5,500
people (mainly in Cheltenham) and recruits graduates all year round into entry
level roles in a huge range of operational functions.

While the work is totally unique, the skills and professional qualifications
gained will be industry standard, and transferable. Everyone benefits from a
personalised training programme. Applicants must be British citizens.

INVESTORS IN PEOPLE

Look a little deeper.

IT, Internet, ICT Research, Information Assurance, Mathematics, Language and Culture specialists | c.£25,000 + benefits

Sponsored Undergraduate Technologist scheme | c.£18,600 + benefits

All roles based in Cheltenham

Take a closer look at the world. Conflict, terrorism, military action and the increasing use of the internet are posing a growing number of threats to UK interests. Here at GCHQ we use the latest and most exciting technology to counter those threats, as well as providing world class advice and consultancy on information security issues to customers in government and industry.

You'll help us gather and interpret information – using your analytical skills and creative thinking to strip back the layers and provide vital, life saving intelligence. In return, you'll enjoy a rare insight into global affairs – as well as unique opportunities for development.

Help create a safer world by taking a closer look at *our* world of work.

www.careersinbritishintelligence.co.uk

Applicants must be British citizens. GCHQ values diversity and welcomes applicants from all sections of the community. We want our workforce to reflect the diversity of our work.

it's an interesting world

GlaxoSmithKline

www.gsk.com/uk-students

Vacancies for around 40-50 graduates in 2011

- Engineering
- Finance
- IT
- Manufacturing
- Marketing
- Purchasing
- Research & Development
- Sales

Starting salary for 2011
£Competitive

Universities that GlaxoSmithKline plans to visit in 2010-11
Please check with your university careers service for details of events.

Application deadline
Year-round recruitment

Contact Details
Turn to page 248 now to request more information or visit our new website at www.top100graduateemployers.com

GlaxoSmithKline (GSK) is a place where ideas come to life. As one of the world's leading research-based pharmaceutical companies, GSK is dedicated to delivering products and medicines that help millions of people around the world to do more, feel better and live longer.

Based in the UK, with operations in the US and over 100 countries worldwide, GSK makes almost 4 billion packs of medicine and healthcare products every year. And much of this is thanks to an extensive product range that includes everything from prescription medicines and vaccines to popular consumer healthcare products.

So while some people depend on GSK's pioneering pharmaceutical products to tackle life-threatening illnesses, others choose best-selling nutritional brands such as Lucozade and Ribena for a feel-good boost. GSK even manages to brighten smiles with some of the world's favourite toothpaste brands.

But being a leader brings responsibility and means that GSK must also help developing countries where debilitating disease affects millions of people. To meet this challenge, GSK is committed to improving access to medicines where they are needed the most. GSK's new volunteering programme 'PULSE' empowers employees to use their skills and knowledge to make a significant difference in impoverished communities at home or abroad.

New starters at GSK soon see that there's no such thing as a typical career path. With so much geographical and business diversity on offer, as well as a number of industrial placements across all business functions, there are plenty of opportunities to learn and develop. Find out more about the opportunities on offer by visiting GSK at www.gsk.com/uk-students

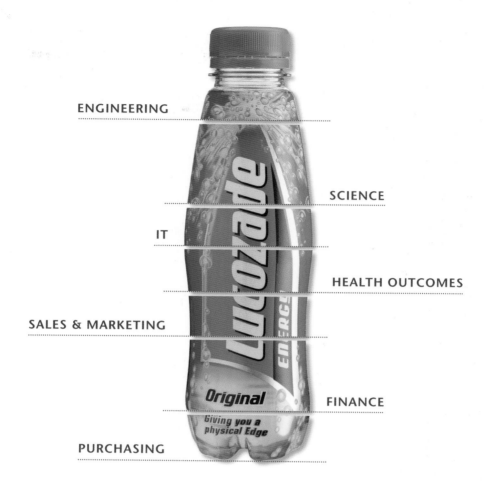

ENGINEERING

SCIENCE

IT

HEALTH OUTCOMES

SALES & MARKETING

FINANCE

PURCHASING

YOU'LL BE AMAZED HOW MUCH GOES INTO OUR PRODUCTS.

Graduate Opportunities: Sales, Marketing, Finance, Science, IT, Purchasing, Engineering and Health Outcomes

It's a fact that science is a vital part of what we do. Look beyond that though, and you'll see everything happening at GSK is a real team effort from beginning to end, where a variety of different specialist departments come together to achieve incredible results. And that means as one of the world's leading research-based pharmaceutical and healthcare companies, we're in a great position to offer a wide range of unmissable opportunities to graduates from any degree background.

*Discover why our success depends on so much more than science. Visit **www.gsk.com/uk-students***

GSK is proud to promote an open culture, encouraging people to be themselves and giving their ideas a chance to flourish. GSK is an equal opportunity employer.

Together we can make life better.

 GlaxoSmithKline

gsk.com/uk-students

Goldman Sachs

www.gs.com/careers

Vacancies for around 300 graduates in 2011

- Accountancy
- Finance
- Investment Banking
- IT

Vacancies also available in Europe, the USA, Asia and elsewhere in the world.

Starting salary for 2011
£Competitive

Universities that Goldman Sachs plans to visit in 2010-11
Please check with your university careers service for details of events.

Application deadline
See website for full details.

Contact Details
✉ emeagraduaterecruiting@gs.com

Turn to page 248 now to request more information or visit our new website at www.top100graduateemployers.com

The Goldman Sachs Group, Inc. is a leading global financial services firm providing investment banking, securities and investment management services to a substantial and diversified client base that includes corporations, financial institutions, governments and high-net-worth individuals. Founded in 1869, the firm is headquartered in New York and maintains offices in London, Frankfurt, Tokyo, Hong Kong and other major financial centres around the world.

Goldman Sachs welcomes graduates from a wide range of university courses and backgrounds. There are a number of different stages when graduates can consider joining Goldman Sachs. Naturally, they will be given different degrees of exposure and responsibility but whether it is as an intern, a new analyst or a new associate, successful applicants will immediately become part of the team with a real and substantial role to play.

Academic discipline is less important than the personal qualities an individual brings with them, however a strong interest in and appreciation of finance is important. Whatever the background, it is intellect, personality and zest for life that the firm values the most.

Goldman Sachs evaluate candidates on six core measures – achievement, leadership, commercial focus, analytical thinking, team work and the ability to make an impact. The firm expects commitment, enthusiasm and drive from its employees, but in return, offers unparalleled exposure, early responsibility, significant rewards and unlimited career opportunities.

Goldman Sachs

First job.
Lasting impression.

A chance. An opportunity. A foot in the door. At Goldman Sachs, your first job will give you more. You'll gain access to unparalleled training programs. Work alongside some of the smartest minds in the financial industry. And gain hands-on experience that will serve you right now, and for years to come. Learn how to make a lasting impression on your career at **gs.com/careers**

Goldman Sachs is an equal opportunity employer. © The Goldman Sachs Group, Inc., 2010. All rights reserved.

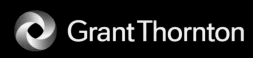
Grant Thornton

www.grant-thornton.co.uk/graduates

Vacancies for around 250 graduates in 2011

■ Accountancy

■ Finance

Vacancies also available in Europe and elsewhere in the world.

Starting salary for 2011
£Competitive
Varies depending on location.

Universities that Grant Thornton plans to visit in 2010-11

Bath, Birmingham, Bristol, Cambridge, Cardiff, Durham, Leeds, London, Loughborough, Manchester, Nottingham, Oxford, Sheffield, Warwick
Please check with your university careers service for details of events.

Application deadline
No deadline for UK

Belfast: 29th October 2010.
Early applications are encouraged from 1st September 2010.

Contact Details

Turn to page 248 now to request more information or visit our new website at www.top100graduateemployers.com

Dave Prentice, 22 - Trainee Auditor
Spotted playing football with workmates at 5.45pm

EXPOSED
THE TRUTH ABOUT CORPORATE CULTURE

Grant Thornton is the UK's fifth largest accountancy firm. With 28 UK locations and 4,000 staff, they provide advice to clients of every description. As part of a global firm with a presence in over 100 different countries, they can also offer graduates opportunities for international exposure.

The firm is focused on being a bold and positive leader, both within its chosen markets and within the accounting profession in general. In 2010 they were named Auditor of the Year in the FD's Excellence Awards.

Graduates can apply for positions in a number of different business areas: Audit, Tax, Business Risk Services, Actuarial and Recovery & Reorganisation. Trainees are encouraged to take ownership and drive their development by putting their new skills into practice straight away. So whether they are working with a household name or a smaller client, graduates will often be face-to-face with finance directors, business owners and influential non-executive directors.

The graduate scheme is designed to help successful applicants become qualified professionals as smoothly and quickly as possible. Graduates start their career with the national induction programme. Further training is held at a dedicated learning centre, Bradenham Manor, where graduates gain essential business, technical and professional skills. Individually focused career development will feature specialist and managerial training and, for some people, progression to partnership.

Trainees work across a variety of sectors and within different teams to develop a range of skills. Secondments and transfers are also commonplace, so there are opportunities to work in different parts of the business and abroad.

For more information, please go to: www.grant-thornton.co.uk/graduates

"When it came to the training, I wasn't just impressed by the surroundings"

EXPOSED
THE TRUTH ABOUT TRAINING

Amy Lucas, 24 - Business Risk Trainee
Spotted preparing her presentation on the lawn at Bradenham Manor, our 17th century training centre

Accountancy careers for business-minded graduates

Get behind the scenes at Grant Thornton and you'll discover a graduate employer like no other. It's not just that we offer some of the very best training in the industry. Or that we encourage our graduates to gain early responsibility on a truly broad portfolio of clients. It's also our energetic, straight-talking culture – one that's perfect for graduates looking for real challenge. Start your own investigation at **www.grant-thornton.co.uk/graduates**

Audit • Tax • Advisory

© 2010 Grant Thornton UK LLP. All rights reserved. Grant Thornton UK LLP, a limited liability partnership. Grant Thornton UK LLP is a member firm within Grant Thornton International Ltd.

Herbert Smith

www.herbertsmithgraduates.com

Vacancies for around 85 graduates in 2011

For training contracts starting in 2013

 Law

Starting salary for 2011
£38,000

Universities that Herbert Smith plans to visit in 2010-11

Belfast, Birmingham, Bristol, Cambridge, Cardiff, Dublin, Durham, Edinburgh, Exeter, Glasgow, Leeds, Leicester, London, Manchester, Newcastle, Nottingham, Oxford, Reading, Sheffield, Southampton, St Andrews, Strathclyde, Warwick, York
Please check with your university careers service for details of events.

Application deadline
July 2011
See website for full details.

Contact Details
graduate.recruitment@herbertsmith.com
020 7374 8000

Turn to page 248 now to request more information or visit our new website at www.top100graduateemployers.com

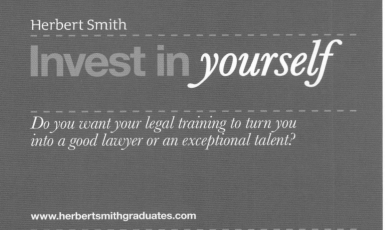

Herbert Smith

Invest in *yourself*

Do you want your legal training to turn you into a good lawyer or an exceptional talent?

www.herbertsmithgraduates.com

Herbert Smith in association with Gleiss Lutz and Stibbe

Pre-eminent in dispute resolution and with an outstanding reputation for high-value transactional advice, Herbert Smith LLP is a leading international law firm. Its main clients are prominent global and national businesses that it serves from a network of offices in Asia, Europe and the Middle East.

Herbert Smith's international client offering is enhanced by its alliance with leading European law firms Gleiss Lutz and Stibbe and by associations with Al-Ghazzawi Professional Association in Saudi Arabia and Hiswara Bunjamin & Tandjung in Indonesia.

Alongside the firm's reputation in dispute resolution and corporate, it has leading practices in finance, real estate, competition and employment, pensions and incentives. It is also acknowledged as a leader in a number of industry sectors, including the energy and natural resources and financial institutions sectors.

The breadth of Herbert Smith's practice, its technical and commercial expertise and the consistently high quality of its broader service are all factors cited by clients when they choose Herbert Smith to advise them on their most complex disputes, transactions and projects.

The training process balances contentious and non-contentious work; early responsibility and support. An emphasis is also placed on professional and personal development, with the firm running a mentoring scheme as well as its own legal development programme.

Trainees rotate around four six-month seats, including a seat in areas like IP, tax, trusts, EU/ competition, employment, pensions and incentives or the advocacy unit. Trainees can also go on secondments to a client or to one of the firm's international offices. Herbert Smith's global reach makes this a possibility for many.

Herbert Smith

Invest in

yourself

Do you want your legal training to turn you into a good lawyer or an exceptional talent?

For more information on our training programme and vacation schemes, and for details on how to apply, please visit our website at:

www.herbertsmithgraduates.com

Herbert Smith in association with Gleiss Lutz and Stibbe

Hogan Lovells

www.hoganlovells.com/graduates

Vacancies for around 90 graduates in 2011

For training contracts starting in 2013

■ **Law**

Starting salary for 2011
£37,000

Universities Hogan Lovells plans to visit in 2010-11

Birmingham, Bristol, Cambridge, Durham, Exeter, Leeds, London, Manchester, Nottingham, Oxford, Sheffield, Warwick, York

Please check with your university careers service for details of events.

Application deadline
31st July 2011

Contact Details

✉ recruit@hoganlovells.com

Turn to page 248 now to request more information or visit our new website at www.top100graduateemployers.com

Hogan Lovells is one of the leading global law firms with over 40 offices in Asia, Europe, Latin America, the Middle East and the United States. Its distinctive market position is founded on its exceptional breadth of practice and on deep industry knowledge. It advises many of the world's largest corporations, financial institutions and government organisations.

Hogan Lovells' international strength across a wide range of practice areas gives them an exceptional reputation not only for corporate transaction work, but for other specialist areas including litigation, government regulatory, dispute resolution, banking, intellectual property, employment, EU/competition, and tax.

Trainees spend six months in four different areas of the practice to gain as much experience as possible. All trainees must spend six months in a corporate or finance group, and six months gaining contentious experience in the firm's litigation practice. There is also the opportunity to go on secondment to one of the firm's international offices or one of its major clients in the second year of training. Trainees are offered as much responsibility as they can handle as well as a comprehensive skills training programme, regular reviews, appraisals and support. After qualification, continuous training and professional development remain a priority.

Hogan Lovells recruits up to 90 trainee solicitors per year and 50 summer vacation scheme students. Applications are welcome from both law and non-law candidates. The firm recruits high-calibre graduates who can demonstrate strong academic and intellectual ability, ambition, drive, strong communication and interpersonal skills, and a professional/commercial attitude.

Hogan Lovells

VENTURE
MYRIAD
ASTUTE
BELONG

Venture v. to embark upon a journey
– *Your venture at Hogan Lovells can take you all over the world.*

With over 40 offices across the world, you'll have real opportunities to practice international work during your training contract and post qualification. Our genuinely global business means that you will be working with some of the brightest legal minds across the world, enabling you to contribute at the highest level.

Our firmwide team delivers quality as standard and is committed to our clients' ongoing success. To find out more about Venture, Myriad, Astute and Belong at Hogan Lovells visit our graduate website www.hoganlovells.com/graduates.

www.hoganlovells.com/graduates

"Hogan Lovells" or the "firm" refers to the international legal practice comprising Hogan Lovells International LLP, Hogan Lovells US LLP, Hogan Lovells Worldwide Group (a Swiss Verein), and their affiliated businesses, each of which is a separate legal entity. Hogan Lovells International LLP is a limited liability partnership registered in England and Wales with registered number OC323639. Registered office and principal place of business: Atlantic House, Holborn Viaduct, London EC1A 2FG. Hogan Lovells US LLP is a limited liability partnership registered in the District of Columbia.
The word "partner" is used to refer to a member of Hogan Lovells International LLP or a partner of Hogan Lovells US LLP, or an employee or consultant with equivalent standing and qualifications, and to a partner, member, employee or consultant in any of their affiliated businesses who has equivalent standing. Rankings and quotes from legal directories and other sources may refer to the former firms of Hogan & Hartson LLP and Lovells LLP. Where case studies are included, results achieved do not guarantee similar outcomes for other clients. New York State Notice: Attorney Advertising.

© Hogan Lovells 2010. All rights reserved.

The world's local bank

INTERNATIONAL MANAGEMENT PROGRAMME
UK GRADUATE PROGRAMMES

www.hsbcgraduatecareers.com

Vacancies for around
200 graduates in 2011

- Finance
- General Management
- Logistics
- Marketing
- Sales

Vacancies also available in Europe,
the USA, Asia and elsewhere in
the world.

Starting salary for 2011
£Competitive

Universities that HSBC
plans to visit in 2010-11

Aston, Bath, Cambridge,
Cardiff, Durham, Edinburgh,
Lancaster, Leeds, Leicester,
Liverpool, London,
Loughborough, Manchester,
Nottingham, Oxford,
Sheffield, Warwick
Please check with your university
careers service for details of events.

Application deadline
See website for full details.

Contact Details
Turn to page 248 now to request more
information or visit our new website at
www.top100graduateemployers.com

Headquartered in London, HSBC is one of the largest
banking and financial services organisations in the world.
The organisation's international network comprises around
8,000 offices in 88 countries and territories in Europe, the Asia-
Pacific region, the Americas, the Middle East and Africa.

HSBC provides a comprehensive range of financial services to over 100 million
customers worldwide in Personal Financial Services, Commercial Banking,
Global Banking and Markets, and Private Banking.

HSBC recruits only the most talented graduates, from any discipline, who
can display the talent and ability to progress to management and executive
positions across the business.

The HSBC International Management (IM) programme offers a globally
mobile generalist banking career that is unrivalled in the industry.
IMs change role and location every 18 months – two years throughout their
career with assignments spanning customer groups and operational regions.
IMs develop a unique set of skills and experiences and are expected to
demonstrate the capability to become the future leaders of the HSBC Group.

HSBC's diverse UK Graduate Programmes offer early responsibility,
recognition of achievement and competitive rewards. They are challenging
and provide opportunities for graduates to realise their full potential.
Each programme is completely different, offering its own unique possibilities
and providing an award winning range of careers.

HSBC Bank UK also offers a range of internships to promising undergraduates
in their first and penultimate year of study, as well as a small number of
placement year opportunities.

world class careers
for world class people

International Management Careers

www.hsbc.com/imcareers

HSBC offers a diverse range of graduate programmes with each providing its own unique set of rewards and challenges

We are looking for the most talented individuals to join us in 2011 and start building a career that could span the breadth of our businesses and the countries & territories in which we operate.

You'll need to demonstrate leadership, agility, unlimited potential and the capability & drive to progress quickly.

• For UK Graduate Programmes visit
www.jobs.hsbc.co.uk/graduates

• For International Management visit
www.hsbc.com/imcareers

We are an equal opportunities employer and seek to employ a workforce which reflects the diverse community at large.

The world's local bank

Issued by HSBC Bank plc. This advert is for recruitment purposes only.

The world's local bank

GLOBAL BANKING AND MARKETS
GLOBAL ASSET MANAGEMENT
GLOBAL PRIVATE BANKING
GLOBAL TRANSACTION BANKING

www.hsbcnet.com/campusrecruitment

**Vacancies for around
200 graduates in 2011**

■ Finance
■ Investment Banking

Vacancies also available in the USA
and Asia.

The new centre of the world.
Today's China is generating enough
economic activity to drive
neighbouring emerging markets
and to sustain developed
economies during the current
slowdown. HSBC is acting
as the bridge to the rest of the
world for this emerging giant.

**Starting salary for 2011
£Competitive**

**Universities that HSBC
plans to visit in 2010-11**
Birmingham, Bristol,
Cambridge, Durham,
London, Manchester
Nottingham, Oxford, Warwick
Please check with your university
careers service for details of events.

**Application deadline
8th November 2010**

Contact Details
✉ hsbc@graduaterecruitment
services.co.uk
Turn to page 248 now to request more
information or visit our new website at
www.top100graduateemployers.com

The HSBC Group is one of the largest banking and financial
services organisations in the world, with 295,000+ employees
serving customers in 88 countries and territories around the
world. With well-established businesses in Europe, Asia-
Pacific, the Americas, and the Middle East and Africa, HSBC's
unique combination of local knowledge and international
expertise reflects its position as 'the world's local bank'.

Through its businesses – Global Banking and Markets, Global Asset
Management, Global Private Banking, and Global Transaction Banking
– HSBC offers a comprehensive range of financial services to high net worth
individuals, corporate, institutional and government clients worldwide.
HSBC takes a long-term approach to their clients and invests time in building
strong relationships and understanding each client's financial requirements.

For high calibre, creative and motivated graduates with a genuine interest in
global finance, the willingness to take on real responsibility and the desire to join
HSBC at this exciting time in its business, HSBC offers a wide range of graduate
and internship opportunities in the following business areas: Global Banking
and Markets, Global Asset Management, Global Private Banking and Global
Transaction Banking.

The extensive and structured programme offers comprehensive business and
technical training as well as the opportunity to learn about its international culture
and gain a range of transferable soft skills. In addition, graduates will work
alongside some of the finest professionals in the industry, taking advantage of
the organisation's extensive financial strength and international network.

Clear waters, China

Speaking the language, Mexico

Branching out, UAE

Capitalise on the moment

Brazil's natural resource

In the midst of the global steel slump, Brazil, South America's largest steel producer, didn't lose sight of the future. HSBC played a significant role in helping Brazilian steel companies harness the situation to bolster their international position, ensuring they were well-equipped for the resumption of demand.

Opening new markets, Indonesia

Driving investments, India

Continued growth, Russia

This advert is for recruitment purposes only

Analyst Programmes 2011
More opportunities.
More than an investment bank.

Our position as a pioneer in emerging markets combined with our truly global presence means there has never been a better time for graduates to join HSBC:

Global Banking and Markets
Global Asset Management
Global Private Banking
Global Transaction Banking

So capitalise on this moment and visit our website to find out more.

www.hsbcnet.com/campusrecruitment

The world's local bank

**Vacancies for around
200 graduates in 2011**

- Accountancy
- Consulting
- Finance
- General Management
- IT
- Sales

Starting salary for 2011
£27,000-£32,000

**Universities that IBM
plans to visit in 2010-11**
Aston, Bath, Birmingham,
Bristol, Brunel, Cambridge,
Cardiff, City, Durham,
Edinburgh, Exeter, Glasgow,
Kent, Lancaster, Leeds,
Leicester, Liverpool,
London, Loughborough,
Manchester, Newcastle,
Northumbria, Nottingham,
Nottingham Trent, Oxford,
Oxford Brookes, Plymouth,
Reading, Sheffield,
Southampton, St Andrews,
Surrey, Warwick, York
Please check with your university
careers service for details of events.

Application deadline
Year-round recruitment

Contact Details
✉ graduate@uk.ibm.com

Turn to page 248 now to request more
information or visit our new website at
www.top100graduateemployers.com

Do you want to build a career?

Do you want to make a difference?

Do you want to be inspired?

Think IBM is just a technology company? Then think again.
IBM is an ideas company – one of the best in the world.
Operating across diverse business streams, they embrace
innovation at every turn, from Consulting, Sales and
Development to IT and Technology.

Making the planet smarter, not only for clients, but for society as a
whole, their team quite literally changes the way the world works with
smart cities, smart banking, smart food, smart energy, smart retail and
smart education.

They also have a pretty smart graduate scheme that challenges and
stretches people on a daily basis and offers fantastic support and genuine
responsibility from day one. Whether it's early contact with clients, applying
learning to the world of business or giving something back to the community
– IBM can offer graduates all this and more.

So, what are IBM looking for? Successful graduates stand out for their
imagination, adaptability, drive, teamwork and boundless energy. They can
come from any degree background, providing they are expecting a 2:1 and
are passionate about their area of expertise.

The journey begins with an induction programme that's supported by ongoing
training to make sure everyone has the personal, business and technical skills
to take their career wherever they want it to be. So, it's no wonder then that
they've been voted the Target Graduate Employer of the Year for three years,
and The Times Graduate Employer of Choice for IT for 10 years.

Think about a smarter future. Think IBM.

Are you ready for IBM?

Opportunities for graduates and interns

Join us. At IBM, you'll use your learning and imagination to bring innovation to life and make the planet smarter. Every day, you'll be challenged and inspired as you impact upon live projects and work with the latest technologies and some of the brightest minds around the globe. This is a place where you'll grow, develop and take responsibility for creating solutions that will change the world. A place where you'll receive amazing training and support, and there's no limit to what you can achieve.

Let's build a smarter planet.
ibm.com/start/uk

J.P.Morgan

jpmorgan.com/careers

Vacancies for around 300 graduates in 2011

- Finance
- Investment Banking
- IT

Vacancies also available in Europe, the USA and Asia.

Starting salary for 2011
£Competitive

Universities J.P. Morgan plans to visit in 2010-11
Please check with your university careers service for details of events.

Application deadline
7th November 2010

Contact Details
Turn to page 248 now to request more information or visit our new website at www.top100graduateemployers.com

From the start, J.P. Morgan's goal has been to become the world's most respected, successful and influential investment bank. Two hundred years on, this hasn't changed. J.P. Morgan is an industry innovator, setting the pace of change in global finance, executing 'first-class business, in a first-class way'.

So what does this mean for future colleagues? To put it simply, the opportunity to work with some of the finest minds and develop an outstanding career in a leading global financial services firm.

Graduate and internship opportunities are available across all areas – Investment Banking, Sales, Trading & Research, IB Risk, Asset Management, Private Banking, Finance, Operations & Business Services, and Technology.

Each training programme combines on-the-job learning with classroom instruction that is on a par with the world's finest business schools. Graduates and interns gain exposure to different parts of the business, to give them a multidimensional perspective of the company. As a result, they emerge not only with a thorough grounding in a particular business area, but a broad experience of the wider commercial picture and a range of transferable business skills.

J.P. Morgan is looking for team-players and future leaders with exceptional drive, creativity and interpersonal skills. Impeccable academic credentials are important, but so are achievements outside the classroom.

More information and helpful advice about graduate careers and internship opportunities can be found at jpmorgan.com/careers

Our strength is your opportunity.

Our strong position in the market has been built on the character and intelligence of our people. To maintain that strength, we are committed to recruiting and developing top talent. This means that if you want to really advance your career, you should become part of our team. It's our goal to make sure you achieve your goals.

Graduate deadline: November 7, 2010
Summer internship deadline: December 12, 2010

Apply via the Europe section of our careers website.

 jpmorgan.com/careers

J.P.Morgan

J.P. Morgan is a marketing name of JPMorgan Chase & Co. and its subsidiaries worldwide.
©2010 JPMorgan Chase & Co. All rights reserved. J.P. Morgan is an equal opportunities employer.

JAGUAR

LAND- -ROVER

www.jaguarlandrovercareers.com

Vacancies for around 135 graduates in 2011

- Accountancy
- Engineering
- Finance
- Human Resources
- IT
- Logistics
- Manufacturing
- Marketing
- Purchasing
- Research & Development
- Sales

THERE'S NO MISTAKING QUALITY.

Starting salary for 2011
£27,000

Universities that Jaguar Land Rover plans to visit in 2010-11

Aston, Bath, Birmingham, Bristol, Brunel, Cambridge, Durham, Leeds, Loughborough, Manchester, Nottingham, Sheffield, Southampton, Warwick
Please check with your university careers service for details of events.

Application deadline
31st December 2010

Contact Details

Turn to page 248 now to request more information or visit our new website at www.top100graduateemployers.com

Innovation, quality, performance and premium. Since conception, Jaguar Land Rover has been redefining the boundaries of luxury motoring. Each of these brands is a clear market leader in its field, known and desired the world over. Less well-known perhaps, is the quality of their 2 year graduate programme. Yet this too displays the same hallmarks of excellence as their exceptional vehicles.

Jaguar Land Rover is a business with an unparalleled heritage, and an exciting future. To maintain its market-leading status, it needs to be at the forefront in everything it does. So, far from being just about engineering, the graduate programme recruits for every function in the business – from Product Development Engineering, Manufacturing, IT and HR, through to Marketing, Finance and Purchasing.

Mirroring the stature of their vehicles, standards are high with no room for compromise. Jaguar Land Rover are looking for graduates who won't accept second best, who have the confidence and initiative to drive this business forward and enjoy the personal development this brings. Whichever area they join, the focus is on excellence and performance throughout. The programme begins with a thorough introduction to both the Jaguar and Land Rover brands, followed by carefully planned personal development. This will include assignments in different areas of the business and, in most functions, the support and funding necessary to achieve professional status.

As would be expected from an internationally successful business, the rewards and benefits are equally outstanding, and include a competitive salary and pension scheme, joining bonus and an employee car purchase scheme.

FINISH IS EVERYTHING.

CAN YOU THINK OF A BETTER PLACE TO START?

**Product Development Engineering • Finance • Purchasing
Manufacturing • IT • HR • Marketing, Sales and Service**

When you make some of the world's most luxurious cars, every tiny detail counts.
And you'll be pleased to hear that we devote exactly the same level of attention to you
and your future with us. Whatever your degree, we offer highly exceptional careers
for high performing graduates.

For more information please visit our website **www.jaguarlandrovercareers.com**

John Lewis Partnership

www.jlpjobs.com/graduates

**Vacancies for around
65 graduates in 2011**

- Finance
- IT
- Retailing

Starting salary for 2011
£24,000-£24,500

**Universities that the
John Lewis Partnership
plans to visit in 2010-11**
Durham, Edinburgh, Leeds,
Loughborough, Warwick
Please check with your university
careers service for details of events.

Application deadline
26th November 2010

Contact Details
✉ recruitment_waitrose
@waitrose.co.uk
Turn to page 248 now to request more
information or visit our new website at
www.top100graduateemployers.com

The John Lewis Partnership is unique. One of the reasons
for this is that the business puts the happiness of its people
– its Partners – at the heart of everything it does.

The business has evolved a distinct brand of retailing that customers
recognise and trust. Alongside this, they've grown to become experts in
training, developing and nurturing graduates into some of the industry's most
successful professionals and managers.

The John Lewis Partnership runs a number of graduate schemes.
These include retail management schemes at Waitrose, Britain's favourite
retailer, and John Lewis, the UK's largest department store group.
Additionally, the Partnership offers the opportunity to support John Lewis
in Buying and Merchandising schemes, and the whole business in their
Head Office based IT and Finance schemes.

Both Waitrose and John Lewis are looking for people who are passionate
about becoming managers on the shop floor. But while they share principles
of quality, service and value, these are distinct businesses, working in different
but equally challenging ways. Meanwhile, The Partnership's Head Office is
focused on those who'd like to develop specialist expertise in key functions.

Because everyone who works for the John Lewis Partnership co-owns it as
a Partner, graduates will find the opportunity to shape the way the business
is run and to share in its profits. And whichever training scheme is chosen,
successful applicants will come to work each day knowing their wellbeing is
looked after. Not just through a host of exceptional benefits, but in the spirit of
Partnership and mutual respect.

John Lewis Partnership | Waitrose | John Lewis

Graduate ambitions.
Great reputations.
The Partnership
starts here.

**Retail Management, Buying, Merchandising,
IT and Finance Graduate Schemes.**

There's a good reason why Waitrose, John Lewis and our
Head Office teams have gained such great reputations
for quality and service. Everyone who works here co-owns
our business as a Partner. It's why we're called the John
Lewis Partnership — and if you join us on one of our
graduate training schemes, you won't just find outstanding
support and development. You'll get a say in the way we're
run and a share in our profits too. Of course, this means
more responsibility. We'll be expecting plenty of drive,
initiative and fresh ideas from you. After all, that's what
makes a great Partnership.

If you've the potential to be a great Partner,
find out more at jlpjobs.com/graduates

The John Lewis Partnership operates without discrimination
and embraces diversity; this is reflected in all that we do.

**Vacancies for around
900 graduates in 2011**

- Accountancy
- Consulting
- Finance
- Human Resources
- IT

Starting salary for 2011
£Competitive

**Universities that KPMG
plans to visit in 2010-11**

Aberdeen, Aston, Bath,
Birmingham, Bristol,
Cambridge, Cardiff, Durham,
Edinburgh, Exeter, Glasgow,
Lancaster, Leeds, Leicester,
Liverpool, London,
Loughborough, Manchester,
Newcastle, Nottingham,
Oxford, Reading, Sheffield,
Southampton, St Andrews,
Strathclyde, Warwick, York
Please check with your university
careers service for details of events.

Application deadline
Year-round recruitment

Contact Details

✉ ukfmgraduates@kpmg.co.uk

Turn to page 248 now to request more
information or visit our new website at
www.top100graduateemployers.com

At KPMG, the people make the place. And what's that place
like exactly? In short, it's one where everyone feels valued,
and hard work is recognised and rewarded.

It's also a place that's growing. Since a number of European firms merged
to form KPMG Europe LLP, they have become the largest fully-integrated
accountancy firm in Europe, offering Audit, Tax and Advisory services to
everyone from oil companies to music gurus.

But it's not just what KPMG does that's important. It's the way that they do
it. The values don't just live on a wall. They're a way of life, underpinning the
way KPMG works with clients and with each other.

So what can graduates look forward to at KPMG? Exposure to clients from
day one. Working on challenging projects. And if they're studying for a
professional qualification, there's a fantastic support network that includes
a mentor and generous study leave.

Despite the focus on qualifications, it's not all work and no play.
Whether it's joining societies and sports teams or enjoying volunteering
days, free lunches and secondment opportunities, KPMG is a fantastic
place for graduates to start developing their technical and personal skills.

KPMG would like to hear from graduates with at least a 2:1 degree in
any discipline. And, once they've applied, they can expect a response on
the next working day.

To stand out from the crowd, graduates need to apply early. Head straight
for www.kpmg.co.uk/careers

No spin.

Straight talking from KPMG.

**Graduate Programmes
All degree disciplines**

We close for applications once we
are full. To secure a place at KPMG,
be sure to apply early. To find out
more head straight to:

www.kpmg.co.uk/careers

THE SUNDAY TIMES
25
BEST BIG
COMPANIES
TO WORK FOR
2010

AUDIT ▪ TAX ▪ ADVISORY

KPMG

© 2010 KPMG LLP, a UK limited liability partnership, is a subsidiary of KPMG Europe LLP and a member firm of the KPMG network of independent member firms affiliated with KPMG International, a Swiss cooperative.

make today delicious

www.kraftfoods-ukgraduates.co.uk

Possible Vacancies in 2011

- Engineering
- Finance
- Human Resources
- IT
- Logistics
- Manufacturing
- Marketing
- Research & Development
- Sales

Vacancies may also be available in Europe.

Starting salary for 2011
£Competitive

Universities Kraft Foods plans to visit in 2010-11
Please check with your university careers service for details of events.

Application deadline
See website for full details.

Contact Details
✉ graduates@kraftfoods.com

Turn to page 248 now to request more information or visit our new website at www.top100graduateemployers.com

Where can you make a delicious difference, everywhere?

Kraft Foods is everywhere. As one of the world's largest food and beverage companies – with a huge range of delicious products across 70 different countries – its global portfolio of household-name brands are delivered through the talent of its people. Now that Kraft Foods has joined forces with Cadbury, opportunities for graduates couldn't be more tempting.

This meeting of minds has brought the best of both worlds, to create a new three-year Graduate Programme (as well as a number of Industrial Placements), that give graduates real responsibility from day one – together with structured training that will expose them to an outstanding portfolio of iconic brands, designed to give graduates a unique experience tailored to their own particular needs.

This unrivalled development programme will excite and challenge in equal measure. Successful applicants will undertake a series of placements that will provide valuable and wide-ranging experience in a world-class commercial enterprise: equipping them with the expertise and knowledge to build a senior-level management career, in the UK and beyond.

Graduates will enjoy the support and advice of their buddy and mentor – and be inspired by the fact that both Kraft Foods and Cadbury have a proud tradition of developing future leaders of their business from their Graduate Programme. Ultimately, of course, it will be down to graduates as to how far they will go. Their drive, energy and commercial spirit, together with their passion and enthusiasm are just the foundation on which they will have every chance to succeed – and make a delicious difference, everywhere.

L'ORÉAL

Vacancies for around 30 graduates in 2011

- Finance
- Logistics
- Marketing
- Sales

Starting salary for 2011
£28,000

Universities that L'Oréal plans to visit in 2010-11

Bath, Bristol, Cambridge, Dublin, Durham, Edinburgh, London, Loughborough, Manchester, Nottingham, Oxford, Warwick

Please check with your university careers service for details of events.

Application deadline
Year-round recruitment
See website for full details.

Contact Details
Turn to page 248 now to request more information or visit our new website at www.top100graduateemployers.com

Graduates joining the L'Oréal management training scheme will be given real responsibility, real challenges and real opportunities from day one. With 130 products sold per second worldwide, L'Oréal offers the most ambitious and entrepreneurial graduates the chance to work with, and become, the most inspirational minds in the business.

L'Oréal's stimulating, motivating and diverse culture is key in making it the No. 1 FMCG employer of choice across Europe (Universum Student Survey, 2010). L'Oréal is a committed Investor in People and is ranked among the top 40 most sustainable companies in the world (Forbes, 2010). With brands that reach over 1 billion people in more than 130 countries every year, L'Oréal's global scope is perfectly suited to graduates pursuing exciting, international business careers.

The L'Oréal Management Training Scheme comprises a personalised, 12 month development programme and includes professional training in 12 business disciplines. Over the year, Management Trainees will work in three different areas of L'Oréal's business to help maximise their potential and prepare them for future leadership. They could find themselves masterminding a launch strategy for one of its world renowned brands, such as Diesel or Armani, or negotiating with buyers at Britain's largest retailers. Or perhaps they'd be more suited to tackling the logistical challenges presented by a company that produces over 4.5 billion products annually, or to managing part of L'Oréal's €17.5 billion revenue.

Based in London, L'Oréal offers a host of excellent benefits, including healthcare, sports teams and fantastic social events. Find out more at www.lorealbusinessclass.co.uk

VOTED No.1 FMCG EMPLOYER ACROSS EUROPE*

* BUSINESS STUDENTS & HUMANITIES STUDENTS, UNIVERSUM SURVEY, 2010

"WITHIN FOUR WEEKS I WAS MANAGING MY OWN BRAND"

Timi, Commercial Management Trainee 2010
2:1 International Business with French, Warwick University

RÉAL OPPORTUNITY

You've got energy, imagination and a passion for business. These same qualities define L'Oréal, one of the world's most successful FMCG companies. Our industry-leading, 12 month training scheme gives you the opportunity to discover different areas of our business before you specialise, allowing you to develop and maximise your own potential.

With offices in over 60 countries, L'Oréal offers truly global opportunities in:

Commercial • Marketing • Supply Chain • Finance

Our internship scheme comprises both summer and sandwich placements in the UK and abroad.

Find out more at **LOREALBUSINESSCLASS.CO.UK**

INVESTORS IN PEOPLE | Silver

L'ORÉAL
WELCOME TO THE RÉAL WORLD

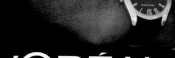

L'ORÉAL PROFESSIONNEL PARIS   MATRIX   KÉRASTASE PARIS   RALPH LAUREN   REDKEN 5TH AVENUE NYC   GARNIER   Kiehl's SINCE 1851   DIESEL FOR SUCCESSFUL LIVING

MAYBELLINE NEW YORK   SOFTSHEEN-CARSON   GIORGIO ARMANI PARFUMS   VIKTOR&ROLF   cacharel PARIS   shu uemura   LANCÔME PARIS

PUREOLOGY   L'ORÉAL   BIOTHERM   MIZANI   SKINCEUTICALS

Quality products. Quality people.

www.lidl.co.uk

Vacancies for around 20 graduates in 2011

- General Management
- Purchasing
- Retailing
- Sales

Starting salary for 2011
£33,000
Rising to £53,000 after three years.

Universities that Lidl plans to visit in 2010-11

Aston, Bath, Cardiff, Exeter, Glasgow, Lancaster, Leeds, Leicester, Loughborough, Manchester, Newcastle, Nottingham, Reading, Southampton, Strathclyde
Please check with your university careers service for details of events.

Application deadline
Year-round recruitment

Contact Details
✉ recruitment@lidl.co.uk

Turn to page 248 now to request more information or visit our new website at www.top100graduateemployers.com

As one of the UK's retail success stories, Lidl's simple retail philosophy and efficient working practices allow them to focus on what they do best – providing top quality products at the lowest possible prices.

Lidl is an established international food retailer with more than 8,000 stores trading across Europe. With over 550 stores in the UK alone they have an impressive schedule of new store openings.

Uncompromising on quality, Lidl looks for the same in their graduates. The Graduate Area Management Programme is open to all degree disciplines. The programme covers all aspects of retail management from store operations to logistics, supply chain, property and most importantly, people management. A structured and hands-on approach to training allows graduates to take on early responsibility with support being provided throughout the training by experienced colleagues.

At Lidl, initiative is encouraged with achievements being recognised; this is supported by their promise that internal candidates come first in all career opportunities. In fact, nearly all their senior professionals started their careers in store operations and have successfully progressed in career paths such as sales, property, construction, logistics and a wide range of head office positions.

Lidl is seeking talented, motivated and ambitious people who are excellent communicators and possess good commercial awareness.

For further information, please visit www.lidl.co.uk

Quality products. Quality people.

Star Quality?

Can you deliver star qualities? If you can lead and inspire as
a part of a team, take the next step now towards applying
to work for a world-class retailer.

For more information or to download our graduate
brochure, please visit **www.lidl.co.uk**

www.lidl.co.uk

Linklaters

www.linklaters.com/ukgradsTT

**Vacancies for around
110 graduates in 2011**
For training contracts starting in 2013

 Law

Vacancies also available in Europe,
the USA and Asia.

Starting salary for 2011
£37,400

**Universities Linklaters
plans to visit in 2010-11**
Birmingham, Bristol,
Cambridge, Cardiff, Durham,
Edinburgh, Exeter, Glasgow,
Leeds, Liverpool, London,
Manchester, Newcastle,
Nottingham, Oxford,
Sheffield, St Andrews,
Warwick, York
Please check with your university
careers service for details of events.

Application deadline
See website for full details.

Contact Details
Turn to page 248 now to request more
information or visit our new website at
www.top100graduateemployers.com

Linklaters is one of the world's most prestigious law firms –
a network of exceptionally talented, highly motivated lawyers,
working as a team to fulfil their ambition of becoming the
premium global law firm.

While many law firms are strong in particular areas, Linklaters is the only firm to
have market-leading global teams across the full range of corporate, finance
and commercial practice areas. This, partnered with a culture of innovation,
teamwork and entrepreneurship, means that they are asked to advise the
world's leading companies, financial institutions and governments on their
most important and challenging transactions and assignments.

A truly global firm, Linklaters has 19 practices across 26 cities, giving
graduates the opportunity to connect with a diverse range of international
colleagues and clients on a daily basis. As part of the training contract,
trainees have secondment opportunities to one of the firm's international
offices or to a client's office.

Non-law graduates spend a conversion year at law school taking the Graduate
Diploma in Law (GDL) and all graduates complete the Legal Practice Course
(LPC) before starting their training contracts. The firm meets the cost and
provides a maintenance grant for both. The training contract is structured
around four six-month seats, designed to build knowledge, experience and
contacts in a broad range of practice areas and to equip graduates for a
long-term career.

Linklaters has high expectations of its trainees and recruits talented and
motivated graduates. In return, they offer trainees global opportunities,
world-class training and incredible rewards.

LLOYD'S

www.lloyds.com/tt100

Vacancies for around 10 graduates in 2011

Finance

General Management

Starting salary for 2011
£26,000

Universities that Lloyd's plans to visit in 2010-11
Bath, Bristol, Cambridge, Durham, London, Oxford, Warwick, York
Please check with your university careers service for details of events.

Application deadline
See website for full details.

Contact Details
✉ graduate.enquiry@lloyds.com
Turn to page 248 now to request more information or visit our new website at www.top100graduateemployers.com

As the world's leading specialist insurance market, Lloyd's handles some of today's toughest and most complex risks – like hurricanes, terrorism, cyber-crime and political unrest. Lloyd's is relied upon by organisations, governments and individuals in more than 200 countries and territories worldwide.

Lloyd's 18-month graduate programme offers a series of placements throughout the Corporation of Lloyd's and the market it oversees, giving graduates the chance to experience and influence many different aspects of what Lloyd's does – from business strategy and underwriting through to market operations. It is a chance to work with and learn from highly intelligent and experienced people, gaining a unique and panoramic view of Lloyd's, the global insurance industry and business in general.

This is a generalist scheme, aimed at offering a tailored, personal approach to development, and giving graduates a formidable range of highly marketable skills. Through internal and external courses, group learning and on-the-job development, graduates will develop expertise in communicating, influencing and presenting; learn to manage projects, increase their commercial awareness and make a direct impact; and at the end of the scheme, take advantage of a range of opportunities available.

Lloyd's programme is designed for high-calibre graduates with a well-rounded set of skills. Graduates who are creative, analytical, flexible, enthusiastic, and adept at communicating – whatever the degree discipline or university – are encouraged to apply.

WE ARE
LLOYD'S OF
EXCEPTIONAL
TALENT

For over 300 years, governments, organisations and individuals have relied on us to tackle some of the world's toughest and most unusual risks. When Nelson sailed into battle, we were there; when the Titanic embarked on its fateful maiden voyage, we were there; and when the first commercial space flight soars into the Earth's atmosphere, we will be there too. This is why we are looking for only the most exceptional talent to join our graduate programme. Join our scheme and you will experience the extraordinary variety of activity that goes on at Lloyd's. You will develop not only specialist insurance skills but powerful business knowledge. More than anything, you will contribute to Lloyd's legendary reputation for expertise. Explore more at our website.

WWW.LLOYDS.COM/TT100

LLOYDS BANKING GROUP

www.lloydsbankinggroup.com/talent

Vacancies for around 150 graduates in 2011

- Finance
- General Management
- Human Resources
- Investment Banking
- IT

Starting salary for 2011
£28,000-£31,000

Universities that Lloyds Banking Group plans to visit in 2010-11

Aston, Bath, Birmingham, Bristol, Cambridge, Durham, Edinburgh, Exeter, Lancaster, Leeds, London, Loughborough, Manchester, Newcastle, Nottingham, Oxford, Warwick, York

Please check with your university careers service for details of events.

Application deadline
See website for full details.

Contact Details
Turn to page 248 now to request more information or visit our new website at www.top100graduateemployers.com

There is so much more to a career at Lloyds Banking Group. With over 140,000 employees, serving over 30 million customers across 40 countries, Lloyds Banking Group is proud to be one of the UK's leading financial services organisations. With an impressive number of well-known brands, Lloyds Banking Group is offering graduates something very different.

With such a diverse portfolio of brands, it's no surprise Lloyds Banking Group has the career opportunities to match. With the Graduate Leadership Programme (GLP), Internships and Direct Entry Graduate roles, graduates and undergraduates will find a path that both challenges and develops them. Opportunities span across the business, giving a broader understanding of how the organisation works.

The aim of the GLP is to nurture leadership potential, enabling graduates to excel and progress to senior management. Everyone will have access to a dedicated Emerging Talent Manager to support them on their totally unique career journey. Development will include formal training; one-to-one reviews and placements which are designed to build up management skills and leadership qualities. Depending on the programme, study towards professional qualifications will form part of the package.

Successful applications will need a minimum 2:1 in any discipline, together with all the qualities that make for strong leaders: judgement; drive; the ability to influence and successfully put plans and ideas into action. As well as exceptional development opportunities, graduates can expect a comprehensive rewards and benefits package. Opportunities like this are rare. The chance to build an extraordinary career and at a critical time in the bank's development.

UNDERLINING
THE DIFFERENCE

GRADUATE AND UNDERGRADUATE OPPORTUNITIES

Lloyds Banking Group is like no other organisation. Our scale, our vision, our commitment and our culture. We have a unique offering for our customers, our investors and for you too. The differences between a career here and at any other organisation are clear. Nowhere will you get the same scope for self development and the same experiences. Nowhere will you be part of such a huge, industry-defining integration. Nowhere will you enjoy the same influence and challenge.

When it comes to our graduate opportunities, it's not just the scale that sets us apart. It's the lasting relationships we build, complex concepts we simplify and the extra mile we travel.

We offer Graduate Leadership Programmes in the following areas:

• Business Technology • Corporate Markets • Finance • HR • General Management

See the difference for yourself. Visit **www.lloydsbankinggrouptalent.com**

We value
diversity and
always appoint
on merit.

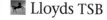

YOUR M&S

www.marksandspencer.com/gradcareers

Vacancies for around 185 graduates in 2011

- General Management
- Human Resources
- IT
- Logistics
- Purchasing
- Retailing

Starting salary for 2011
£23,500-£25,000
Plus benefits.

Universities that Marks & Spencer plans to visit in 2010-11

Aston, Bath, Birmingham, Cambridge, Cardiff, Durham, Lancaster, Leeds, London, Loughborough, Manchester, Oxford, Oxford Brookes, Strathclyde, Surrey
Please check with your university careers service for details of events.

Application deadline
See website for full details.

Contact Details
✉ graduate.opportunity
@marks-and-spencer.com
Turn to page 248 now to request more information or visit our new website at
www.top100graduateemployers.com

Graduates don't need to work at M&S to have a special relationship with them. Just ask their millions of customers. But those who join the M&S graduate programme gain a unique insight into the hard work, expertise and passion that goes into creating one of the UK's best-loved retailers. Whichever way graduates look at it, it's the perfect platform from which to build a rewarding long-term career – and a place they'll be proud to call home.

The M&S graduate programme offers a range of opportunities across their different business areas. For graduates who are interested in retail management, it will take them to Commercial Manager level in 12 months, while the Head Office programme has roles in a range of areas, from IT and Food Technology, to Merchandising and Logistics. Either way, successful applicants will be on the right path to a successful career – one that will give them the chance to shape and grow their business.

M&S expect a lot from its graduates. High standards. Hard work. And a genuine commitment to doing the right thing for customers and colleagues. So it only makes sense graduates should expect plenty back in return. That's why M&S are investing more then ever in the rewards they offer. Not just a competitive salary and the essential benefits that are expected from a leading employer like M&S. But also a range of flexible rewards that successful applicants can tailor to their individual needs.

To find out more and apply, visit www.marksandspencer.co.uk/gradcareers

YOUR M&S

www.marksandspencer.com/gradcareers
We are M&S. Are you?

Whichever way you look at it, retail is a challenge. So it takes a special sort
of person to take their place on the M&S graduate programme. But if you
love thinking on your feet and can take the fast pace in your stride, there's
simply nowhere better to build a rewarding long-term career.

Retail Management · HR · IT · Buying · Merchandising
Product Technology & Design · Logistics · Business Placements
And more...

B. Hooked on the pace already

A. Questioning whether you can keep up

YOUR M&S

MARS

Vacancies for around 30 graduates in 2011

- Engineering
- Finance
- General Management
- Purchasing
- Research & Development

Starting salary for 2011
£29,000-£31,000

Universities that Mars plans to visit in 2010-11
Please check with your university careers service for details of events.

Application deadline
February 2011
See website for full details.

Contact Details
Turn to page 248 now to request more information or visit our new website at www.top100graduateemployers.com

Makers of characters you'd love to rub shoulders with.

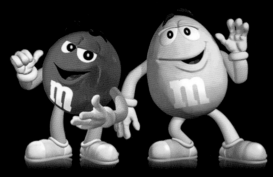

Mars®, Uncle Ben's®, Whiskas®, M&M's®, Dolmio®, Pedigree®, Maltesers®, Extra®... these are just some of the iconic brand names that form the global, $40bn Mars portfolio, making it one of the world's biggest consumer goods companies.

However, it's the unique culture that truly separates Mars from the competition. Over 60,000 associates in more than 106 countries enjoy a degree of freedom and responsibility unparalleled in the business world.

Still a family-run business and privately owned, Mars is able to invest its profits back into developing the organisation. This means graduates have the freedom to think differently and the ability to do things that convention wouldn't ordinarily allow. In fact, Mars graduates get all the support, autonomy and responsibility they need to become iconic in their own right.

Ultimately, it's the graduates that will drive projects or their roles forward and shape the business. Whether their talents lie in research & development, engineering, finance, procurement or general management, Mars' renowned development programmes offer responsibility from day one.

Graduates are placed in real roles that are carefully chosen to suit their development needs and enjoy support in pursuing professional qualifications through financial sponsorship, study leave and regular two-way feedback.

Mars view personal development as important as delivering results, so their graduate programmes provide extensive learning and development opportunities outside of the day-to-day job, along with strong individual mentoring. This allows talented individuals an opportunity to take their career in their own hands while also getting the expert guidance that has seen Mars develop industry-leading figures.

Uncle Ben's®
"Perfect every time"

Pedigree®

Mars®

DOLMIO®

whiskas®

Galaxy®

i'm lovin' it

www.mcdonalds.co.uk/careers

Vacancies for around 150 graduates in 2011

■ General Management
■ Retailing

Starting salary for 2011
£18,500-£21,500

Universities McDonald's plans to visit in 2010-11
Please check with your university careers service for details of events.

Application deadline
Year-round recruitment

Contact Details
✉ mcdcareers@uk.mcd.com
☎ 020 8700 7007

Turn to page 248 now to request more information or visit our new website at www.top100graduateemployers.com

Forget the myth that says McDonald's only offers McJobs. The reality is very different – and far more interesting. McDonald's management careers offer exceptional challenge and support, some excellent rewards and all the potential of a world-famous brand.

Their 20-week management development programme prepares graduates for running a restaurant – Business Management as they call it. This is commercial management in its fullest sense. Graduates gain valuable operational experience in the restaurants, and, as importantly, benefit from wide-ranging commercial exposure. They cover everything from leadership and people development to cash control and profit maximisation.

Provided they excel on the programme, within a few years of joining, graduates could be managing a £million business with a 60-strong team: a McDonald's restaurant. After that they join a management career path that could lead to Executive team level. Naturally, not everyone will climb that high. But as long as they have leadership potential and can make the most of the award-winning training, there's no reason why graduates shouldn't set their sights high.

McDonald's urges graduates to do some soul-searching before applying. McDonald's managers set the tone of their restaurants, bringing the best out of their team. To build their businesses, they have to display energy, commitment and hard work every day. And they need to combine both decisiveness and sensitivity; ideas and action. Only by blending all these qualities will graduates excel on one of the most stimulating management development programmes around.

I love that I can go right to the top.

PAUL, ESSEX

MY MᶜJOB

Trainee Business Managers

With management training that reflects the latest thinking and wins awards, your career can go as far as you want it to.

Apply at **mcdonalds.co.uk/careers**

© 2009 McDonald's. The Golden Arches and i'm lovin' it logos are trademarks of McDonald's Corporation and affiliates.

McKinsey&Company

www.mckinsey.com/careers

Vacancies for no fixed quota **of graduates in 2011**

■ Consulting

Vacancies also available elsewhere in the world.

Starting salary for 2011
£Competitive

Universities that McKinsey & Company plans to visit in 2010-11
Bath, Bristol, Cambridge, Dublin, Edinburgh, London, Oxford
Please check with your university careers service for details of events.

Application deadline
31st October 2010

Contact Details
✉ london_opportunities@mckinsey.com
☎ 020 7961 7070

Turn to page 248 now to request more information or visit our new website at www.top100graduateemployers.com

McKinsey & Company helps world-leading clients in the public, private and third sectors to meet their biggest strategic, operational and organisational challenges. Their goal is to provide distinctive and long-lasting performance improvements – in short, it is about having an impact. Making a difference.

As a consultant in this truly global firm, graduates will have the opportunity to work with colleagues and clients from all around the world. They will come into contact with CEOs, government leaders and the foremost charitable organisations, and work together with them on their most exciting and challenging issues.

Working as part of a small team, and dedicated to one project at a time, graduates will be fully involved from the very start of their first project. No two weeks will be the same: from gathering and analysing data, to interviewing stakeholders or presenting findings to clients, the range of industries and business issues to which successful applicants have exposure will mean that they are constantly acquiring new skills and experience. Bright, motivated newcomers can expect their ideas and opinions to be encouraged and valued, right from day one.

Graduates will also enjoy world-class personal and professional development. Formal training programmes, coupled with a culture of mentoring and coaching, will provide the best possible support.

Working in consulting is challenging, but McKinsey encourages a healthy work-life balance. Successful applicants will find like-minded individuals, and a thriving range of groups, initiatives and events that bring people together.

McKinsey&Company

Building global leaders

We welcome applications from all degree disciplines
To find out more please visit www.mckinsey.com/careers

METROPOLITAN POLICE

www.metpolicecareers.co.uk

Vacancies for around TBC graduates in 2011

- Accountancy
- Finance
- General Management
- Human Resources
- IT
- Marketing
- Media
- Research & Development

Starting salary for 2011
£Competitive

Universities that the Met plans to visit in 2010-11
London
Please check with your university careers service for details of events.

Application deadline
Year-round recruitment

Contact Details
Turn to page 248 now to request more information or visit our new website at www.top100graduateemployers.com

The Metropolitan Police Service (MPS) is continually evolving and improving to respond to the needs of millions of people of all nationalities, faiths and cultures who visit, live and work in London. The organisation aims to deliver quality policing that reduces crime – and the fear of crime – across the capital. It is also recognised on a global scale as a leading authority on policing today.

The MPS today is a far cry from the organisation that was founded in 1829 by Home Secretary Sir Robert Peel. Back then, there were just 1,000 officers looking after a population of 2 million. Now, there are some 55,000 officers and staff who make up the MPS, working as one team to make the streets safer for 7.2 million Londoners in 32 boroughs across 620 square miles.

As one of the capital's largest employers, the MPS is committed to having a workforce that reflects the community it serves. People join from all kinds of backgrounds, bringing all sorts of skills and experience to a huge diversity of roles. As well as frontline officers, the MPS employs 14,000 police staff who carry out vital work such as answering emergency calls, forensics, handling finances or harnessing the latest advancements in technology.

But London can only be policed with the trust and respect of all Londoners, so it's essential that everyone who joins has the sensitivity to work effectively with the many different communities that make up the capital.

Making London safer is uniquely challenging but uniquely rewarding. Good salaries are supplemented by attractive benefits including a superb pension and opportunities for career progression.

BE THERE FOR LONDON

VOLUNTEER AS A POLICE OFFICER

16 hours a month · Opportunities across London

Volunteer as a police officer for just 16 hours a month and experience the challenge and satisfaction of frontline policing. Wear the same uniform and carry the same powers as a regular police officer. Train for one of the most varied and fascinating volunteering roles around. Put your skills to the test, develop existing talents and discover new ones. Be a highly trained special constable. Be there for London.

To find out more and apply online visit **www.metpolicecareers.co.uk/specials** quoting ref: 132/10 on your application. If you have any further queries please contact our Recruitment Call Centre, Mon-Fri, 9am-4pm, on **0845 727 2212**.

METROPOLITAN POLICE

NEW SCOTLAND YARD

SECURITY SERVICE MI5

www.mi5.gov.uk/careers/graduates

Vacancies for around TBC graduates in 2011

- Engineering
- Finance
- Human Resources
- IT
- Law
- Purchasing

Starting salary for 2011
£24,750
Varies by function.

Universities that MI5 plans to visit in 2010-11
Please check with your university careers service for details of events.

Application deadline
Year-round recruitment

Contact Details
✉ careers @recruitmentoffice.org.uk
☎ 0845 450 2152

Turn to page 248 now to request more information or visit our new website at www.top100graduateemployers.com

MI5 safeguards the United Kingdom against threats to national security. Talented graduates from a range of backgrounds and degrees join MI5 for demanding, stimulating and rewarding careers.

Many become Intelligence Officers, moving postings every few years to take on new challenges, gain different experience and expand their understanding of MI5's work. Others join as Intelligence Analysts, Digital Intelligence Specialists, in other IT roles and in the Language Unit. Together they work on investigations assessing threats, solving complex digital intelligence problems, manipulating data, spotting connections and identifying patterns. Team working, outstanding communication skills and finely-balanced judgement are critical.

The culture at MI5 is professional, friendly and informal. Being able to establish rapport with a variety of people, recognise problems and suggest solutions in a collaborative working environment are essential. Honesty and integrity are expected from all staff and strong organisational skills, attention to detail and commitment to self-development are important.

Although MI5 does not offer a bespoke graduate programme, it provides extensive training and development opportunities. This improves job satisfaction and promotion prospects and increases people's deployment opportunities for exposure to a broader spectrum of work. Postings may take people to legal, policy or resources departments and there are opportunities to work in the regional offices or Northern Ireland.

MI5 offers a generous holiday entitlement, pension and flexible working where operational commitments allow. Some sites have subsidised fitness facilities and staff restaurants. Applicants must be British citizens and limit those they tell about their application to immediate family and/or their partner.

my neighbours don't realise I help protect national security

INTELLIGENCE OFFICERS LONDON £24,750 + BENEFITS

Discretion is vital at MI5, the UK's security intelligence agency. Few people will know about the role you'll play in helping to safeguard national security. Every day you'll be making informed decisions that contribute towards MI5's efforts in countering terrorism, espionage, sabotage and the spread of weapons of mass destruction. Only you and your team will know you're protecting your community's way of life, and that's all that matters.

Whatever your degree, it's likely we have something that suits your skills and abilities. We are looking for highly capable, persuasive and analytical graduates with the confidence and resilience to handle a high level of responsibility early in your career. You will be supported by managers, peers and mentors and encouraged to expand your skill set through our careers academy, personal and professional courses and work experience in a range of our departments.

Do you have what it takes to be quietly successful? To find out more about the challenging, interesting and worthwhile careers we offer, visit **www.mi5.gov.uk/careers/graduates**

SECURITYSERVICE
MI5

DESG
DEFENCE ENGINEERING AND SCIENCE GROUP

MINISTRY OF DEFENCE

www.desg.mod.uk

Vacancies for around 75 graduates in 2011

Engineering

Starting salary for 2011
£24,130

Universities that the MOD plans to visit in 2010-11
Please check with your university careers service for details of events.

Application deadline
See website for full details.

Contact Details
✉ dcp-cctmdesgmktman@mod.uk

Turn to page 248 now to request more information or visit our new website at www.top100graduateemployers.com

The Defence Engineering and Science Group (DESG) is the team of thousands of engineers and scientists working within the Ministry of Defence.

The UK needs modern battle winning forces to defend its interests and to contribute to strengthening international peace and security. Cutting-edge engineering and science is a critical component in supporting this effort. The MOD is proud to offer graduates the opportunity to join what is probably the very best graduate development scheme for engineers and scientists in the UK: The Ministry of Defence, Defence Engineering and Science Graduate Scheme.

This prestigious graduate scheme is accredited by: IET, IMarEST, IMechE, RINA, IoP, RAeS and ICE and has been an industry leader for almost thirty years, launching hundreds of graduates into satisfying careers in engineering and science. It is because of the requirement to safeguard the UK and its interests that the DESG can offer a huge range and depth of development opportunities – making it a market leader.

Moreover, it is the quality of the training programme, the accelerated path to chartership, personal mentoring and considerable investment in each graduate that sets this apart from competitors in the engineering and science field. The DESG Graduate Scheme is a carefully structured but flexible training programme; enabling each graduate to get the most from a series of training courses and work placements (including placements with industry).

Through this unique scheme each graduate is able to further their professional development – making it possible for them to gain tremendous engineering or science experience and to achieve Chartered status within just four years.

MINISTRY OF DEFENCE

Engineering's
Top gear.

The UK requires modern, battle winning forces to defend its interests and to contribute to strengthening international peace and security. These forces increasingly depend on scientific and technological advances to maintain their ability to operate effectively; this means the provision of technologies of tremendous speed, power and capacity to deliver a decisive operational edge.

We are: The Ministry of Defence, Defence Engineering and Science Group.

Organisation Description: Central Government. The DESG is the team of thousands of engineers and scientists within the MoD.

DESG offers you many benefits including:

1. Probably the very best graduate development scheme for engineers and scientists available in the UK
    – fully accredited by IMechE, IET, ICE, RINA, RAeS, IoP and IMarEST.

2. Considerable investment in support of your personal professional development;
    along with a wide range of exciting placement opportunities (including placements in industry).

3. An accelerated path to Chartered status in your engineering or science profession;
    with the DESG it's possible for you to achieve professional Chartership in just four years.

4. A truly rewarding career. MoD projects are fascinating, valuable, unique and sometimes highly classified.

Degree Disciplines required: A multitude of engineering disciplines, sciences (with an emphasis on physics) and surveying.

Applications: Apply on-line via our website (click 'How to Apply'). See www.desg.mod.uk for closing date.

Undergraduate Sponsorship: Visit our website (click 'Student Opportunities' for details).

www.desg.mod.uk

The MoD is an Equal Opportunities Employer.

Morgan Stanley

www.morganstanley.com/careers

Vacancies for around
250 graduates in 2011

- Finance
- Investment Banking
- IT

Vacancies also available in Europe, the USA, Asia and elsewhere in the world.

Starting salary for 2011
£Competitive

Universities that Morgan Stanley plans to visit in 2010-11
Please check with your university careers service for details of events.

Application deadline
Varies by function
See website for full details.

Contact Details
✉ graduaterecruitmenteurope
@morganstanley.com
Turn to page 248 now to request more information or visit our new website at
www.top100graduateemployers.com

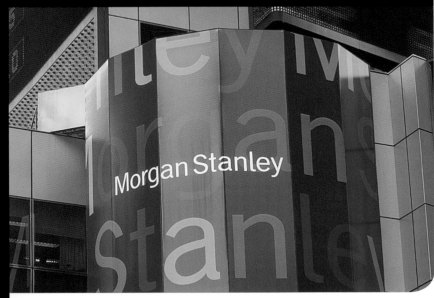

Morgan Stanley is a leading global financial services firm providing a wide range of investment banking, securities, investment management and wealth management services. The Firm has over 60,000 employees in more than 1,300 offices in 42 countries, serving clients worldwide including corporations, governments, institutions and individuals.

The Analyst Training at Morgan Stanley is designed to provide its graduates with the knowledge and toolkit they require to quickly become effective professionals. Through a structured programme, graduates learn how to use Morgan Stanley's unsurpassed data resources and analytical tools, as well as gain a thorough understanding of the firm's culture, its core values and key products.

Morgan Stanley offers Graduate Programmes in Investment Banking, Global Capital Markets, Sales & Trading, Equity Research, Real Estate Investing, Credit Risk Management, Private Wealth Management, Technology, Finance & Operations.

In addition to the common skills requirements of interpersonal, communication, team working and confidence, graduates should focus on developing their negotiating, networking and entrepreneurial skills. Additionally, given today's globalisation in the marketplace some divisions have demand for graduates with fluency in a number of foreign languages. All candidates will be required to work hard and be incredibly focused. Needless to say, a real appetite for the job must be demonstrated with a proven track record of work and academic experience.

Morgan Stanley accepts applications from all disciplines, with a 2:1 class degree or equivalent.

Day 1: Introductions

Day 2: The World

Morgan Stanley is an equal opportunity employer committed to workforce diversity. © 2010 Morgan Stanley

The faster your career grows, the smaller the globe will seem.
At Morgan Stanley, solving complex challenges and fueling economic growth across continents is what we do. On any given day, you might be facilitating and underwriting transactions, or providing liquidity and capital for a growing global economy. We offer you a structured path to success, which means you'll quickly gain unprecedented exposure to every aspect of the financial world. Moreover, we'll give you the opportunity to become involved in making a real difference. And we'll provide you with the training, mobility, and responsibility to do it. If you have the perspective to face today's global challenges, we'd like to talk to you.

To find out more about career opportunities at Morgan Stanley and to hear from recent hires visit: **www.morganstanley.com/careers**

Morgan Stanley

www.networkrailgraduates.co.uk

Vacancies for around 135 graduates in 2011

- Accountancy
- Engineering
- Finance
- General Management
- IT
- Logistics
- Purchasing

Starting salary for 2011
£24,500
Plus package.

Universities Network Rail plans to visit in 2010-11
Aston, Bath, Bristol, Cambridge, Durham, Edinburgh, Leeds, Liverpool, London, Loughborough, Manchester, Newcastle, Nottingham, Oxford, Sheffield, Southampton, Strathclyde, Warwick, York
Please check with your university careers service for details of events.

Application deadline
January 2011

Contact Details
✉ enquiry@networkrail.co.uk
☎ 0845 601 4228
Turn to page 248 now to request more information or visit our new website at www.top100graduateemployers.com

No other organisation has such a marked and visible impact on the lives of people across Britain. Responsible for tracks, signals, tunnels, bridges, viaducts, level crossings and stations, Network Rail touches millions of lives across the nation, every day, delivering the better railway that is vital for the economic prosperity of this country.

With high passenger satisfaction levels and record levels of passenger and freight demand, Network Rail's ambition is to continue to meet customer needs while providing even better value for money in the future. As they are delivering some of the largest engineering projects going on across Europe today, they will help redefine both the travel network and Britain's future economic growth.

Few other graduate programmes can boast such huge responsibility. After a period of induction, graduates will gain valuable experience on a range of placements, and they'll have real control over the pace and content of their progression. The Network Rail Graduate Programme has a vast range of schemes that include engineering, finance, operations management, project management and information management (IT).

Network Rail takes training and development very seriously; after all, graduates are about to become the future leaders of the organisation. Whichever the specialism, successful applicants will work towards professional qualifications and will receive regular reviews of their performance and development. Wherever they join, graduates will be able to see the impact of their work around them, every day. As they become part of the organisation that helps to define the nation.

NetworkRail

Create a better future

Every day. Everywhere. We're doing this.

Over the next 10 years, Britain's rail traffic will increase by 30% – making ours the fastest-growing railway in Europe.

The work we carry out today will shape the Britain of tomorrow. By increasing capacity and encouraging innovation, we're creating improvements that will mean more trains, more services and better journeys for everyone. Our work will help Britain reach ambitious carbon emissions targets; it will power the economy.

We offer a range of multi-disciplinary programmes: from finance to engineering, management to IT. Build real experience through varied placements. Have a huge impact on diverse projects, and feel the pride you get from helping to develop the railways of tomorrow.

For more information, please visit networkrailgraduates.co.uk

NATIONAL GRADUATE
DEVELOPMENT PROGRAMME
ngdp
FOR LOCAL GOVERNMENT

www.ngdp.co.uk

Vacancies for around
80+ graduates in 2011

General Management

Starting salary for 2011
£22,958
Plus London weighting.

Universities that ngdp
plans to visit in 2010-11
Please check with your university
careers service for details of events.

Application deadline
10th January 2011

Contact Details

✉ enquiry@ngdp.com

☎ 0845 222 0250

Turn to page 248 now to request more
information or visit our new website at
www.top100graduateemployers.com

"I wanted to deal with issues, not just bottom lines."

Real life. Real work.
Graduate Opportunities in Local Government

The ngdp is a two-year graduate management development programme, run by Local Government Improvement and Development. The programme was set up to provide local government with the high-calibre managers their communities need – and to give committed graduates the training and opportunities to make a positive impact.

Local government is the largest employer in the UK, with over two million staff in over 400 local authorities and in excess of 500 different occupational areas. Since 2002 over 450 graduates have completed the programme and many now hold influential managerial and policy roles. Now is a time of huge change in the sector and trainees will make a real contribution to actually bring those changes about.

The national programme framework is built on a series of placements in key areas within a council and offers a range of experiences and challenges. All of which will provide a broad understanding of different aspects of local government in strategy, front-line service and support. Although employed by a participating authority on a 2-year, fixed-term contract, graduates will also benefit from being part of a national programme group, giving them the opportunity to participate in a national induction event, join an established knowledge-sharing network and take part in an accredited series of learning and development components.

The programme has taken graduates in many different directions. Ultimately, it's a chance to be part of an exciting period of opportunity and not just propose change, but actually make it happen.

"I wanted to work in a community, not just an office."

Graduate Opportunities in Local Government

One of my most rewarding projects involved updating Merton's Ethnic Minority Housing Strategy. It involved a lot of research. The kind of research that meant I was meeting with council leaders, organising community workshops, and going out onto the streets to talk to people about the issues they're facing. Now the new strategy's in place and I have the satisfaction of seeing how it's changing the way people in the area live.

That's what the ngdp is all about. It's a two-year graduate training programme designed to help you develop into a leader in local government. You'll take on a variety of projects. You'll meet all sorts of people. And you'll enjoy all the challenges and opportunities that only come from doing real work.

Find out more about my projects and why you should join us on our website.

Real life. Real work. ngdp.co.uk

NATIONAL GRADUATE
DEVELOPMENT PROGRAMME
ngdp.
FOR LOCAL GOVERNMENT

NHS

www.nhsgraduates.co.uk

Possible vacancies for graduates in 2011

- Finance
- General Management
- Human Resources
- IT

Starting salary for 2011
£Competitive

Universities that the NHS plans to visit in 2010-11
Please check with your university careers service for details of events.

Application deadline
See website for full details.

Contact Details
✉ graduates
@lead.institute.nhs.uk

Turn to page 248 now to request more information or visit our new website at www.top100graduateemployers.com

As career opportunities go, there aren't many organisations that can compete with the NHS. The NHS offers graduates personal challenge and stretch, a range of career opportunities across England, but in addition, it also offers the unique opportunity to make a real difference to people, to society and to the health of the 60 million people in England. Now that really is worth pursuing!

If candidates are driven enough to join the NHS, the NHS will give them comprehensive training and development and challenging work.

However to have a chance of joining the NHS, graduates need to be ready to put patients at the centre of their work and be dedicated to improving the healthcare of England. At the same time, a graduate needs to be an individual with high potential who wants to and is not afraid to: be a leader, challenge the status quo, deliver innovation and improvement, lead culture change and deliver major efficiency savings.

The NHS offers a huge range of exciting and challenging opportunities for people who are passionate about making a difference. No matter what area of the NHS is joined, graduates will become part of a talented, passionate team of people-committed to providing the best care and treatment to patients.

The NHS welcomes applicants from all backgrounds who have or are expecting at least a 2:2 or equivalent.

To discover more about working at the NHS, find helpful advice for job seekers and to search and apply for current vacancies please visit www.jobs.nhs.uk

Are you up for the challenge?

Imagine being responsible for improving the quality of the patient experience.

Are you still up for the challenge?

Think about what it means to make £20 billion savings.

Are you still up for the challenge?

Ask yourself how you would put patients first.

Are you still up for the challenge?

Remember how complex the NHS is.

Are you still up for the challenge?

Search online for "NHS white paper".

Are you still up for the challenge?

Then visit nhsgraduates.co.uk

NHS Graduate Management Training Scheme | www.nhsgraduates.co.uk

Lead the way

www.brightergraduates.com

Vacancies for around 30 graduates in 2011

- Engineering
- Finance
- General Management
- IT
- Marketing
- Sales

Starting salary for 2011
£25,000

Universities that npower plans to visit in 2010-11

Aston, Bath, Bristol, Cambridge, Cardiff, Durham, Exeter, Lancaster, Leeds, Leicester, Liverpool, Loughborough, Newcastle, Nottingham, Reading, Sheffield, Surrey, Warwick
Please check with your university careers service for details of events.

Application deadline
No official deadline
Early application is advised.

Contact Details
✉ graduate.recruitment
@rwebrightergraduates.com
Turn to page 248 now to request more information or visit our new website at www.top100graduateemployers.com

RWE npower is one of the UK's leading integrated energy companies and is part of RWE, one of Europe's largest electricity and gas companies. npower gives creative and ambitious graduates the chance to work on exciting projects.

They operate a portfolio of gas, coal and oil fired power stations in the UK and supply electricity and gas to around 6.8million residential and business customer accounts. npower's sister company, RWE npower renewables, is one of the leaders in renewable energy generation, having developed the UK's first major offshore wind farm and operating hydroelectric power stations in Scotland and Wales. They are committed to conducting their business with a sense of responsibility for the environment, their customers and the communities in which they work.

npower is looking for Britain's brightest graduates. They have opportunities in engineering, business management (sales, marketing and operations), finance, business analysis, quantitative risk and IS within RWE IT UK.

npower is seeking those who will bring enthusiasm, commitment and the capacity to learn, combined with strong analytical and problem-solving skills and will give them the opportunity to shine. npower's graduate programme will introduce successful applicants to the many different facets of their business, and give them responsibility at an early stage within their chosen area of work.

npower is committed to attracting and retaining the best, so all their graduates receive an excellent pay and benefits package, including a competitive starting salary which is reviewed annually.

Which  npower job do you want?

BUSINESS MANAGER

BUSINESS ANALYST

ENGINEER

ACCOUNTANT

RISK ANALYST

At npower we will inspire you to achieve the best in everything you do and play a pivotal role in the company being the best at everything it does. We are looking for bright graduates who have the same drive as us and who are ready for the experience of their life.

There has never been a more exciting time to work in the world of energy generation and supply. npower need graduates to bring inspiration to the way we work; if you can bring enthusiasm, commitment, and the capacity to learn we'll give you the opportunity to shine. Our programme will introduce you to the many different facets of our business, and give you responsibility at an early stage within your chosen area of work.

If this sounds like the graduate job you want, visit our website today.

WHERE WOMEN
WANT TO WORK
2010

visit www.brightergraduates.com

nucleargraduates

www.nucleargraduates.com

Vacancies for around 80 graduates in 2011

- Consulting
- Engineering
- General Management
- Human Resources
- Manufacturing
- Research & Development

Vacancies also available in Europe, the USA, Asia and elsewhere in the world.

Starting salary for 2010
£24,500

Universities that nucleargraduates plans to visit in 2010-11
Please check with your university careers service for details of events.

Application deadline
December 2010

Contact Details
✉ questions @nucleargraduates.com
Turn to page 248 now to request more information or visit our new website at www.top100graduateemployers.com

Ready to explore? Good. There's plenty to discover about nucleargraduates – the most comprehensive graduate programme the energy industry has ever seen. This remarkable two year programme covers engineering, science, business, management and more. And it's open to exceptional graduates from all disciplines and backgrounds.

The UK's nuclear industry is facing its biggest challenge in decades. Existing power stations are nearing the end of their working lives and are ready to be decommissioned. A new wave of plants has been given the go ahead. Nuclear is back on the agenda. That means a new generation of engineers, scientists and business professionals are needed to guide the industry into the future.

It's why the Nuclear Decommissioning Authority, a non-departmental public body, has brought leading businesses and world class organisations, like Rolls-Royce PLC, Sellafield and Magnox, together to create nucleargraduates.

In simple terms, the nuclear sector can be roughly divided into five key areas: decommissioning, power generation, processing, defence and new build. The nucleargraduates programme lets graduates gain experience across all these areas through placements at businesses or organisations based in the UK and internationally. Currently, the programme has opportunities abroad – take Washington DC or Tokyo for example – as well as places much closer to home, like London or Manchester.

Engineering graduates are particularly encouraged to apply and can specialise in Mechanical Engineering, Electrical Engineering and Civil Engineering.

To learn more about the adventure, visit www.nucleargraduates.com or find out what current graduates get up to at www nuclearfootprints.com

Turn a new page by visiting ours

nucleargraduates.com

Engineering • Science • Business • Environment

(Ⓧ) Oxfam

Be Humankind

www.oxfam.org.uk/interns

Vacancies for around 100 graduates in 2011

- Accountancy
- Finance
- General Management
- Human Resources
- IT
- Logistics
- Marketing
- Media
- Purchasing
- Research & Development
- Retailing

Vacancies also available in Europe, the USA, Asia and elsewhere in the world.

Starting salary for 2011
£Voluntary

Universities that Oxfam plans to visit in 2010-11
Please check with your university careers service for details of events.

Application deadline
Year-round recruitment
See website for full details.

Contact Details
Turn to page 248 now to request more information or visit our new website at www.top100graduateemployers.com

Swimming, cinema and socialising with friends...

Few organisations give graduates a genuine chance to make the world a better place. Oxfam does.

By harnessing the power of more than a million staff, volunteers and supporters, it's tackling the big issues. Like helping poor people prepare for the more frequent and severe natural disasters caused by climate change. Helping farmers adapt to the unpredictable weather so they don't go hungry. And pushing governments to come up with a fairer deal for everyone.

It's urgent, vital work. And it calls for passionate, committed, enthusiastic people. People who'll be vocal, take risks and challenge the norm – and who'll be ready to shoulder their share of responsibility. So graduates who join Oxfam's Voluntary Internship Scheme can forget tea rounds and shop runs. The scheme is planned round the precise needs of the organisation. Graduates can have a real impact – whether they volunteer part-time for three, six or 12 months.

The roles could be in Oxfam's Oxford Headquarters, a shop or a regional office. And they range from Deputy Shop Manager to placements in HR or Marketing. But whether graduates help to plan an event, manage a campaign or run a shop, they'll learn just how a major international Non Government Organisation works and enjoy an open culture. And although the work is unpaid, the scheme reimburses reasonable local travel and lunch expenses.

For graduates who want to save lives and campaign for lasting change, it's a fantastic way to build a CV that'll get noticed.

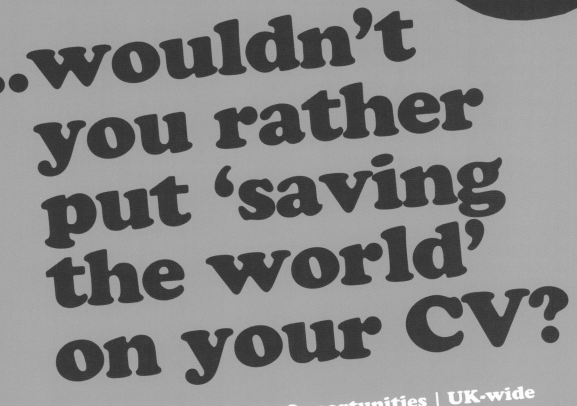

...wouldn't you rather put 'saving the world' on your CV?

Voluntary Internship Opportunities | UK-wide

Right wrongs right here. Take up an internship with an organisation that won't stand for climate change, poverty or injustice – and stand out. Swing into action at **www.oxfam.org.uk/interns**

Oxfam works with others to overcome poverty and suffering.

Oxfam is a registered charity in England and Wales (no 202918) and Scotland (SCO 039042). Oxfam GB is a member of Oxfam International.

Be Humankind

YEARS

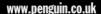
www.penguin.co.uk

**Vacancies for around
30 graduates in 2011**

- Finance
- Human Resources
- Law
- Marketing
- Sales

Starting salary for 2011
£20,413

**Universities that
Penguin Books
plans to visit in 2010-11**
Please check with your university
careers service for details of events.

Application deadline
Year-round recruitment

Contact Details
Turn to page 248 now to request more
information or visit our new website at
www.top100graduateemployers.com

For seventy-five years Penguin has been the publisher
everyone looks to not just for great books, but also for
innovation and for how to act with dignity and integrity.
It is always looking for different points of view, new voices
and ways of working and it is always happy to listen to
new ideas. This diversity among Penguin's workforce has
enabled the organisation to face the challenges of the digital
revolution by ensuring that its content in whatever format
remains the cornerstone of a thriving culture.

Penguin is home to the most trusted brand names in publishing.
Among the Penguin family are Dorling Kindersley, Rough Guides, Michael
Joseph, Hamish Hamilton, Puffin and Ladybird. Penguin has offices in 15
countries across the globe. It publishes a vast array of titles, and its authors
include Jamie Oliver, Nick Hornby, Zadie Smith, Antony Beevor, Eoin Colfer,
Roald Dahl and Marian Keyes.

It is immensely important to Penguin that it attracts top graduate talent,
because the organisation knows the contribution its graduate recruits can
make during their careers. Penguin has a variety of roles across the business
for publicists, production controllers, marketers, designers, accountants,
sales, rights and operations people as well as the traditional editorial and
publishing roles.

Penguin is delighted that its brand continues to attract talent from top
universities, and in return the company strives to provide careers that are
both stimulating and fulfilling for all its employees.

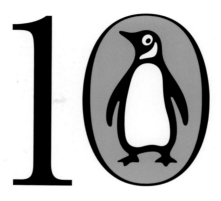

10
REASONS TO
BECOME A PENGUIN

1) You get to work closely with your favourite authors. Now what could be more fun than that? **2) We're a diverse bunch.** And we think publishing should be for everyone. **3) We're the greenest publishers in town.** We work with the Woodland Trust and our books are printed on FSC accredited paper. We even have our own Penguin Wood. **4) Our award-winning publishing.** Over the past year, we have won the Costa Novel Award as well as many other literary accolades including the Wolfson History Prize and the Red House Children's Book Award. **5) We have been around for 75 years.** That's three-quarters of a century of quality publishing. **6) To prove publishing isn't stuffy we play at the cutting edge of the digital revolution.** Check out our vast array of e-book titles and look us up at www.penguin.co.uk to start following us on Twitter, become a fan on Facebook and to have a chat with us on our blog. **7) People pay attention to what we do.** They just do. They can't help it. **8) We're the only publishing company in here.** Go on, check, but don't forget to come and have a chat with us on our blog. **9) You never need to explain what your company does at parties.** When you say 'I work for Penguin', everyone gets just a little bit jealous. **10) Your mum and dad will love you forever ...** (at least that's what our mums and dads tell us).

YEARS

read more
www.penguin.co.uk

COULD YOU?
POLICE

www.policecouldyou.co.uk

Vacancies for unlimited **graduates in 2011**

■ All sectors

Starting salary for 2011
£25,962
On completion of training,
plus excellent pension and benefits.

Universities that HPDS plans to visit in 2010-11
Please check with your university
careers service for details of events.

Application deadline
Year-round recruitment

Contact Details
✉ hpds@npia.pnn.police.uk
☎ 020 7021 7070

Turn to page 248 now to request more
information or visit our new website at
www.top100graduateemployers.com

A career in the police offers an exciting mix of challenge and reward. Policing in today's police service involves reducing crime and the fear of crime, working in partnership with the public, supporting victims and witnesses whilst using the latest technology to assist with the detection and prevention of crime.

The challenges faced by police officers are often mental rather than physical, requiring an understanding of what makes people behave as they do, and to use that knowledge to develop strong policing skills. The modern police force offers a career with many opportunities to specialise in fields from intelligence to investigation.

There are great prospects to move up the career ladder into senior leadership positions. A Cambridge graduate, now a Chief Inspector, said of his decision to become a police officer that when he told his peers he was joining the police it was a conversation stopper, when he sees them now it is a conversation starter.

Graduates who have secured employment as a police officer with one of the forces in England, Wales or Northern Ireland are eligible to apply for the High Potential Development Scheme (HPDS). The HPDS aims to produce a cohort of officers who possess the operational credibility, management skills and strategic awareness to meet the challenges of senior police leadership. The HPDS is delivered in partnership with Warwick University and leads to a Masters Degree in Police Leadership.

Joining the police offers a starting salary of £25,962 p.a. on completion of initial training (additional allowances for officers in London and the South East) and an excellent pensions and benefits package.

For further information about the HPDS go to www.npia.police.uk/hpds

NPIA
National Policing
Improvement Agency

POLICE PLEASE CROSS

We Challenge You

Every single day in the police
service is a challenge. We're
looking for people of outstanding
ability who meet those challenges.

**Take the challenge of your lifetime,
join the police.**

pwc

pwc.com/uk/careers

Vacancies for around 1,000 graduates in 2011

- Accountancy
- Consulting
- Finance
- IT
- Law

Being the one to generate real value

Being the one with the eureka moments

Being the one to rewrite the rulebook

Starting salary for 2011
£Competitive
Plus benefits.

Universities that PricewaterhouseCoopers plans to visit in 2010-11

Aberdeen, Aston, Bath, Belfast, Birmingham, Bristol, Brunel, Cambridge, Cardiff, City, Dublin, Durham, East Anglia, Edinburgh, Exeter, Glasgow, Heriot-Watt, Hull, Kent, Lancaster, Leeds, Leicester, Liverpool, London, Loughborough, Manchester, Newcastle, Nottingham, Oxford, Plymouth, Reading, Sheffield, Southampton, St Andrews, Strathclyde, Surrey, Swansea, Ulster, Warwick, York

Please check with your university careers service for details of events.

Application deadline
Year-round recruitment

Contact Details
☎ 0808 100 1500

Turn to page 248 now to request more information or visit our new website at www.top100graduateemployers.com

PricewaterhouseCoopers LLP helps their clients and their people create the value they want. They work alongside their clients – from public and private companies to governments and charities – to measure, protect and enhance the things that matter most to them. They help their own people to learn, discover, develop and make a real difference throughout their working lives.

They have big ambitions to grow, and for those who are serious about a career in business, they don't believe that anyone else can give graduates a better start. They're proud to say that students agree, voting them number one in The Times Top 100 Graduate Employers survey for the last seven years.

Their people make them stand out as a firm. They choose the best and invest heavily in them. Wherever graduates join them, they'll benefit from training that gives them breadth and depth of knowledge. They will get support to gain a professional qualification, and the chance to experience a range of clients and projects in multiple business areas. Successful applicants can expect a competitive salary and personalised benefits scheme.

They're after the very best. A 2:1 or above in any degree discipline is needed, from 300 UCAS tariff or equivalent. Even more importantly, they're looking for people who can build relationships, put themselves in others' shoes, collaborate, make an impact and shape their own future.

Find out more about their business, the recruitment process and how to apply: pwc.com/uk/careers. For other ways to apply, call 0808 100 1500 or +44 (0)121 265 5852.

Being the one who never stands still

pwc

Helping create value through:

Assurance

Consulting

Tax

Financial Advisory

Actuarial

PwC Legal

You need a 2:1 or above in any degree discipline. From 300 UCAS tariff or equivalent.

We value diversity in our people

To help our clients get the value they want we can never stand still. We need to be constantly challenging ourselves, constantly learning. At PwC we'll give you training, support and access to global experts. You'll be tackling some of the world's toughest issues with great clients – so you're always moving forward.

We work with clients to measure, protect and enhance what matters most to them. Smart, ambitious people able to build strong relationships make us the best at what we do. Students agree: we're proud they've voted us number one in *The Times Top 100 Graduate Employers* survey for the last seven years. Become the best, take a step in the right direction.

Visit pwc.com/uk/careers. Text 'pwc' to 85792 to find your nearest PwC event.*

© 2010 PricewaterhouseCoopers LLP. All rights reserved. "PwC" refers to PricewaterhouseCoopers LLP (the limited liability partnership registered in the United Kingdom), PricewaterhouseCoopers Legal LLP ("PwC Legal", the limited liability partnership registered in the United Kingdom) or, as the context requires, the PricewaterhouseCoopers global network or other member firms of the network, each of which is a separate legal entity.
**Texts charged at your standard network rate.*

P&G

www.pgcareers.com

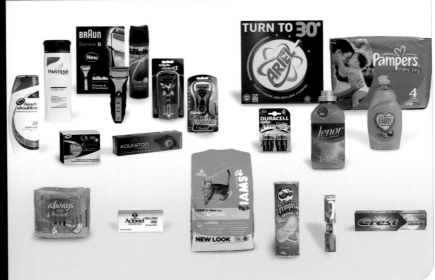

Vacancies for around 115 graduates in 2011

- Accountancy
- Engineering
- Finance
- Human Resources
- IT
- Logistics
- Manufacturing
- Marketing
- Research & Development
- Sales

Vacancies also available in Europe.

Starting salary for 2011
£27,600

Universities that Procter & Gamble plans to visit in 2010-11

Aston, Bath, Birmingham, Bristol, Cambridge, Dublin, Durham, Edinburgh, Exeter, Glasgow, Lancaster, Leeds, Leicester, London, Manchester, Newcastle, Oxford, St Andrews, Strathclyde, Warwick
Please check with your university careers service for details of events.

Application deadline
Year-round recruitment

Contact Details

✉ recunitedkingdm@pg.com

Turn to page 248 now to request more information or visit our new website at www.top100graduateemployers.com

Four billion times a day, P&G brands touch the lives of people around the world. The company has one of the strongest portfolios of trusted, quality, leadership brands, including Pampers, Ariel, Always, Pantene, Mach3, Fairy, Pringles, Lenor, Iams, Crest, Oral-B, Duracell, Olay, Head & Shoulders, Wella, Gillette, Braun and Fusion. The P&G community consists of over 135,000 employees working in over 80 countries worldwide.

P&G attracts and recruits the finest people in the world, because it grows and develops its senior managers within the organisation. This means new starters with P&G can expect a job with responsibility from day one and a career with a variety of challenging roles that develop and broaden their skills, together with the support of training and coaching to help them succeed.

P&G look for more than just good academic records from their applicants. They are looking for graduates who are smart and savvy, leaders who stand out from the crowd, who are able to get things done. They want to hear about achievements at work, in clubs, societies, voluntary and community activities and to see how graduates have stretched and challenged themselves and others. Most functions within the company welcome applicants from any degree discipline. Product Supply requires an engineering degree and R&D requires an engineering or science degree.

To find more details about what the P&G look for, their selection process and the jobs available, go to their website at www.pgcareers.com

We'll help you find your feet and then

GROW
AND GROW...

At P&G, we hire the person, not the position, so we will do all we can to quickly help you become a success.
We guarantee you real responsibility from day one, so you'll immediately play your part in creating best-value products that meet the ever changing needs of our consumers and have a direct impact on a global, $80 billion business.

With nearly 300 of the world's most trusted brands to our name and exciting projects across every area of our business, you can be sure P&G will give you plenty of room for growth.

For information visit
www.PGcareers.com

P&G

Rolls-Royce

www.rolls-royce.com/careers

Vacancies for around 200 graduates in 2011

- Engineering
- Finance
- General Management
- Human Resources
- Logistics
- Manufacturing
- Purchasing
- Sales

Vacancies also available in Europe, the USA and Asia.

Starting salary for 2011
£28,000

Universities Rolls-Royce plans to visit in 2010-11

Aston, Bath, Birmingham, Bristol, Cambridge, Durham, Lancaster, Leeds, London, Loughborough, Manchester, Nottingham, Oxford, Sheffield, Southampton, Strathclyde, Warwick

Please check with your university careers service for details of events.

Application deadline
7th January 2011
Re-opening 7th Feb where appropriate.

Contact Details
✉ HRSharedServiceCentre
@rolls-royce.com
☎ 01332 333333

Turn to page 248 now to request more information or visit our new website at www.top100graduateemployers.com

Most graduates embark on their chosen career with big dreams and ambitions, hoping to make a difference in the world. At Rolls-Royce graduates are not just encouraged to have these high aspirations, but they're put in a position to realise them – daily.

Rolls-Royce is mission-critical in everything they do. Every minute of every day, Rolls-Royce affects the lives of millions of people. They keep 400,000 passengers in the air at any one time. Their Trent 60 gas turbine has been sold to 16 countries and the fleet can generate enough power for three million homes. Over 30,000 commercial and naval vessels operate with Rolls-Royce equipment, keeping coasts, national and international waters safe.

The expertise, diversity and dedication of over 39,000 employees is key. The company is able to attract excellent people because of the specialist skills and knowledge that can be taught to the highest level.

Graduates can choose from two graduate programmes. The Professional Excellence Programme teaches the skills needed to be an expert in a chosen field, learning direct from some of the industry's most experienced professionals. The Leadership Development Programme finds and develops the future leaders of the business. Graduates can expect to achieve a leadership role as early as the fourth year after joining.

Who are they looking for? There's a certain mindset that's shared by all Rolls-Royce people. A relentless desire to make things work better and to redefine the standards everyone else lives by. Whatever the role, graduates will need to show the same passion and collaborative spirit that's underpinned the company's highest achievements.

The difference comes down to the thickness of a human hair.

Engineering · Finance · Supply Chain · Purchasing · Operations Management · HR · Commercial · Customer Management · Project Management

Graduate Opportunities

Our Trent 1000 fan blade requires a precision of design and manufacture that's measured in microns – to the thickness of a human hair. Because when you're engineering each blade to withstand a centrifugal force equivalent to hanging a diesel locomotive from its tip, there is no margin for error. Why not see the difference we could make to your career?

Trusted to deliver excellence

www.rolls-royce.com/careers

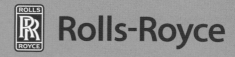

Rolls-Royce

The Royal Bank of Scotland Group

www.makeitrbs.com

Vacancies for around 500+ graduates in 2011

- Accountancy
- Finance
- General Management
- Investment Banking
- IT
- Marketing
- Purchasing
- Retailing
- Sales

Vacancies also available in Europe, the USA, Asia and elsewhere in the world.

Starting salary for 2011
£Competitive
Plus benefit funding.

Universities that The Royal Bank of Scotland Group plans to visit in 2010-11

Aston, Bath, Birmingham, Bristol, Cambridge, City, Durham, Edinburgh, Exeter, Glasgow, Heriot-Watt, Lancaster, Leeds, London, Loughborough, Manchester, Newcastle, Nottingham, Oxford, Sheffield, Southampton, St Andrews, Strathclyde, Warwick
Please check with your university careers service for details of events.

Application deadline
Varies by function
See website for full details.

Contact Details
Turn to page 248 now to request more information or visit our new website at www.top100graduateemployers.com

This is an exciting time to join The Royal Bank of Scotland Group. Graduates joining now will find themselves at the centre of their regeneration, redefining RBS and delivering the solutions that will shape not only their business, but the future of banking.

With a commitment to giving career-building responsibility from day one, RBS is recruiting ambitious graduates who will take their business forward while helping clients' meet their personal objectives.

Few organisations can offer the choice of careers graduates will discover at RBS. The variety of options available across the RBS business is a match for the very best graduate talent.

Programmes offered include: Business & Commercial Banking; Business Services Leadership; Chief Operating Office; Corporate Institutional Banking; Global Banking & Markets; GBM Operations; GBM Technology; Global Restructuring Group; Global Transaction Services; Group Communications; Group Sourcing & Vendor Management; Internships and Placements; Marketing & Innovation; Private Banking & Advice; RBS Finance; RBS Risk; Retail Business Leadership; Security & Risk; Technology Services; Ulster Bank Group and Wealth Management.

Graduates will need a 2:1 or 2:2 depending on programme. Support will be provided via a network of buddies and mentors as well as a first class development programme. They will also have the opportunity to study for professional qualifications.

RBS has vacancies for over 500 graduates and over 500 interns in 2011.

GRADUATE & INTERN CAREERS

**UK, Continental Europe,
Asia Pacific and the US**

RBS has a long history, global strength and is looking to the future with confidence. We are committed to our clients, growing strong relationships and delivering industry leading products and services.

Graduates and interns who join us now will have an influence on the strategic decisions we make going forward. To achieve the extraordinary, and to seize the opportunities at the heart of an organisation that is poised for transformation. With over 30 graduate and intern programmes, from Global Banking & Markets, Finance and Retail Business Leadership to Technology, Marketing and Sourcing & Vendor Management there's something for everyone, whatever their degree discipline or career aspiration.

The place is here. The time is now.
Find out more at **www.makeitrbs.com**

RIGHT PLACE.
RIGHT TIME.

XRBS™
The Royal Bank of Scotland Group

ROYAL NAVY

Vacancies for no fixed quota of graduates in 2011

- Engineering
- Finance
- General Management
- Human Resources
- IT
- Law
- Logistics
- Research & Development

Vacancies also available elsewhere in the world.

Starting salary for 2011
£29,587

Universities that the Royal Navy plans to visit in 2010-11

Aberdeen, Aston, Bath, Birmingham, Bristol, Brunel, Cardiff, Dundee, Durham, East Anglia, Edinburgh, Exeter, Heriot-Watt, Leeds, Liverpool, Loughborough, Manchester, Sheffield, Southampton, Stirling, Surrey, Warwick
Please check with your university careers service for details of events.

Application deadline
Year-round recruitment

Contact Details
☎ 08456 07 55 55
Turn to page 248 now to request more information or visit our new website at www.top100graduateemployers.com

A life at sea has always attracted those with a taste for travel and adventure. But in today's unpredictable job market, there are plenty of other reasons for graduates and final-year students to consider a career with the Royal Navy.

The Royal Navy is, first and foremost, a fighting force, serving alongside Britain's allies in conflicts around the world. It also protects UK ports, fishing grounds and merchant ships and helps combat international smuggling, terrorism and piracy. Increasingly, its 35,000 personnel are involved in humanitarian and relief missions, where their skills, discipline and resourcefulness make a real difference to people's lives.

Graduates are able to join the Royal Navy as Officers – the senior leadership and management team in the various branches, which range from Engineering and Warfare to Medical, the Fleet Air Arm and Logistics. Starting salaries of at least £29,587 compare well with those in industry, with additional pay available for some branches including the Submarine Service and Fleet Air Arm. Those wanting to join the Royal Navy as an Engineer Officer can receive a £12,000 joining bonus (minus tax). What's more, the Royal Navy can offer a secure yet flexible career with the potential to extend to age 50.

The opportunities for early responsibility, career development, sport, recreation and travel exceed any in civilian life. With its global reach and responsibilities, the Royal Navy still offers the chance to see the world, while pursuing a challenging, varied and fulfilling career.

The Royal Navy recruits year-round; current information on the many jobs available can be found at royalnavy.mod.uk/careers

YOU WRITE HISTORY NOT JUST REPORTS

ROYAL NAVY OFFICER

Being an officer in the Royal Navy is a career like any other, but the circumstances and places are sometimes extraordinary. It's a responsible, challenging career that will take you further than you've been before. If you want more than just a job, join the Royal Navy and live a life without limits.

08456 07 55 55
ROYALNAVY.MOD.UK/CAREERS

SAATCHI & SAATCHI

www.saatchi.co.uk/graduate_recruitment

**Vacancies for around
5 graduates in 2011**

Media

**Starting salary for 2011
£Competitive**

**Universities that
Saatchi & Saatchi
plans to visit in 2010-11**
Please check with your university
careers service for details of events.

Application deadline
See website for full details.

Contact Details
Turn to page 248 now to request more
information or visit our new website at
www.top100graduateemployers.com

Saatchi & Saatchi is the world's most famous creative company
and aims to build a culture that creates world changing ideas
designed to inspire participation.

Saatchi & Saatchi has been investing in graduate recruitment schemes
since the 1980s and for the last 10 years has been running a six-week
Summer Scholarship programme. The agency receives hundreds of
applicants, from which 10 are chosen each year to come and work as
trainees, giving them the chance to experience the industry first hand,
and see for themselves exactly what is required for a career in a creative
company. At the end of the six weeks, the agency offers the best
candidates a permanent role at the agency.

In line with the agency's focus on participation, this year's graduate
recruitment scheme was done entirely on Facebook.

The agency created a group, which over 6,000 hopefuls joined, then set a
series of special challenges designed to test certain skills, with applicants
being eliminated after each round. The first challenge was to create a
new Facebook group and encourage as many people as possible to join
in just three weeks. 871 groups were created, with the top two attracting
over 200,000 members each and loads of PR. Other challenges included
choosing a great ad and then recreating it as a video and a Skype interview
with a look-alike of the agency's CEO, Robert Senior.

Taking this slightly unexpected route meant applications were up
400% from 2009. The next graduate recruitment drive will be at the
start of 2011.

NOTHING IS IMPOSSIBLE

SAATCHI & SAATCHI

Sainsbury's

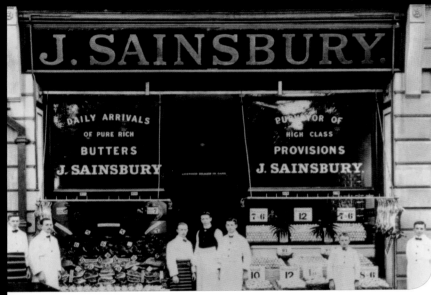

www.sainsburys.co.uk/graduates

Vacancies for around 65 graduates in 2011

- Engineering
- Finance
- General Management
- Human Resources
- IT
- Logistics
- Marketing
- Purchasing
- Retailing

Starting salary for 2011
£25,000-£26,000
Dependent on scheme.

Universities Sainsbury's plans to visit in 2010-11

Bath, Birmingham, Bristol, Cardiff, Durham, Exeter, Lancaster, Leeds, Leicester, Liverpool, Loughborough, Manchester, Newcastle, Northumbria, Nottingham, Reading, Sheffield, Southampton, Strathclyde, Warwick, York
Please check with your university careers service for details of events.

Application deadline
12th December 2010

Contact Details
✉ grad.recruitment
@sainsburys.co.uk
☎ 0845 603 6290

Turn to page 248 now to request more information or visit our new website at www.top100graduateemployers.com

Sainsbury's is not just a food retailer; it is a FTSE 100 business that is proud of its 141 year history of being at the top of British retail. Never one to rest on its laurels, Sainsbury's has exciting plans for the future and is looking for graduates that will get involved to help make these plans happen.

Despite all the economic ups and downs of the last few years Sainsbury's has more than weathered the storm. It has grown and continues to do so – enjoying over five consecutive years of growth and recording sales increases of more than 5% in 09/10, with over 19 million customers shopping with Sainsbury's each week. Sainsbury's have got big plans for the future and they know if they are going to keep growing and make all of these plans reality then they need fresh energy and ideas. Sainsbury's believe that the best ideas can come from anywhere and over the years many of the best have come from its graduates. That's why Sainsbury's graduates are placed into roles that really matter fast – and why good ideas are listened to.

Sainsbury's have a long term commitment to recruiting and developing high calibre graduates. They are looking for a diverse group of exceptional graduates to contribute fresh talent and ideas and to be part of the continued growth and success of the organisation.

For those who are customer-focussed, thrive in a fast paced and dynamic environment and share Sainsbury's company's values, visit www.sainsburys.co.uk/graduates to learn more about the opportunities available and to hear more about the experiences of current Sainsbury's graduates.

We've got big plans.

Right.

And smart graduates help make them happen.

That's what everyone says.

Sure.
But we can prove it...

Last year our sales grew by more than 5%. And our profits by more than 17%. To keep growing we depend on fresh energy and ideas, things that graduates have a lot of. That's why we get graduates into roles that matter fast – and pay attention to good ideas when we hear them. At Sainsbury's it's possible.

Find out how at www.sainsburys.co.uk/graduates

Graduate opportunities 2010/11

Sainsbury's
Try something new today

official partner of the
Paralympic Games

www.shell.co.uk/careers

Vacancies for around 100 graduates in 2011

- Engineering
- Finance
- Human Resources
- IT
- Marketing
- Research & Development
- Sales

Vacancies also available in Europe and Asia.

Starting salary for 2011
£31,950

Universities that Shell plans to visit in 2010-11

Aberdeen, Cambridge, Edinburgh, Heriot-Watt, London, Manchester, Nottingham, Oxford
Please check with your university careers service for details of events.

Application deadline
Year-round recruitment

Contact Details

Turn to page 248 now to request more information or visit our new website at www.top100graduateemployers.com

Whatever new technology the future holds, the world will need plenty of energy to power it and Shell is working on all sorts of ideas to meet the growing demand. With a large number of opportunities in a wide range of commercial and technical roles, they need ambitious graduates to help them tackle the energy challenge.

While a strong academic background is important to Shell, it's not the main consideration. To enable people to thrive in a dynamic and innovative organisation such as Shell, the selection processes are designed to assess the qualities of Capacity, Achievement and Relationship (CAR). Graduates will have the ability to absorb information, analyse problems, make objective decisions and come up with innovative ideas. They will also be enthusiastic and confident, and capable of working in a diverse team. With this in mind, successful applicants display these qualities throughout the process.

Everyone who works for Shell thrives on stimulation and challenge. It offers superb training, support and career choices, and develop potential by teaming all graduates with some of the most accomplished problem solvers in the business.

There are three ways to get a job with Shell: The Gourami Business Challenge, Shell Recruitment Day, or Paid Student Internship, with graduates choosing which route works best for them. Whichever path they take, a comprehensive onboarding programme helps them settle into their new role, and Shell's early career development programme ensures they get off to a flying start. Think further.

SIEMENS

www.siemens.co.uk/graduates

Vacancies for around 40-50 graduates in 2011

- Engineering
- Finance
- General Management
- IT
- Research & Development

Starting salary for 2011
£Competitive

Universities that Siemens plans to visit in 2010-11
Please check with your university careers service for details of events.

Application deadline
Year-round recruitment

Contact Details
☎ 01276 690204

Turn to page 248 now to request more information or visit our new website at www.top100graduateemployers.com

How can a sustainable future be created and a growing population be supported? How can growing energy demands be balanced with the needs of the planet? Big questions demand big answers. And that's what drives everyone at Siemens, one of the world's largest engineering companies.

From healthcare, to industry to energy and the environment, Siemens is working hard to answer the big questions of our time. So graduates looking for a career where they'll be supported, trained and challenged, should join one of their structured two-year Graduate Development Programmes.

As a company, Siemens is proud of its continuous learning environment and its unswerving commitment to innovation. Graduates will see both in action, whether they want to develop a career in Engineering, IT or Business.

Take Business. Successful ones don't run themselves. They take a lot of planning, organising and hard work. Graduates will play an important part in making the Siemens business function, whether they want to develop their career in HR, Finance, Project and Operations Management, or Sales.

The range of Engineering careers on offer within Siemens are as diverse as their industry sectors and projects. From wind power to transportation, broadcast technology to building services, they offer challenging careers for thought-leaders in the sector.

Then there's IT. With a strong track record in delivering some of the UK's most advanced and exciting IT projects, Siemens enjoys long term relationships with some of the best known names in business and public services provision in the UK. Working across the consult, design, build and operate spectrum, they offer an exciting career path for IT graduates looking to pursue a career in the industry.

Final exams are on Monday.
What do we do after that?

Put your theory into practice – at Siemens.

You've earned your degree. And now you've got a head full of ideas. At Siemens, you can turn those ideas into reality. We produce countless innovations year after year for the Industry, Energy and Healthcare Sectors – with highly motivated employees in all kinds of graduate roles across the UK. And soon, perhaps, with you.

siemens.co.uk/grad

SIEMENS

Believe in better

www.workforsky.com

Vacancies for around 50 graduates in 2011

- Accountancy
- Finance
- General Management
- IT
- Logistics
- Marketing
- Media

Starting salary for 2011
£22,000-£26,000+

Universities that Sky plans to visit in 2010-11

Aston, Brunel, Cardiff, City, Glasgow, Loughborough, Manchester, Nottingham, St Andrews, Stirling, Strathclyde, Warwick
Please check with your university careers service for details of events.

Application deadline
See website for full details.

Contact Details
Turn to page 248 now to request more information or visit our new website at www.top100graduateemployers.com

Be a part of history in the making

Sky go beyond imagination. No wonder they're pioneering 3D TV by introducing Europe's first 3D TV channel, one of the most exciting developments in the history of broadcasting. It's all about giving customers the best.

With over 17million viewers in more than 10million households, Sky transform how people watch TV through things like Sky+ and High Definition. Add their award-winning Broadband & Talk and rapidly expanding betting and gaming businesses, and you can begin to see why this FTSE top 30 business has been independently voted the UK's most admired media company.

Sky believe in better, and so do their people. So they look for graduates who are creative. Who want responsibility from the off. Who have the confidence to work alongside people at all levels and have plenty of ambition and initiative. In return, Sky are well-known for giving graduates unparalleled exposure, excellent training and a fun, exciting start to their working life.

Sky see their future talent as vital. The people who join their graduate programmes today can become the business leaders of tomorrow. Sky also offer funding to help graduates get professionally recognised qualifications in their business area – whether that's Customer Operations, Finance, HR, Marketing and Communications, Sky Betting and Gaming, Sky News, Supply Chain or Technology.

To find out more visit www.workforsky.com

Sky delivers some of the most diverse content and services on the planet, and we value the same diversity within our business. We provide a culture of entrepreneurialism and opportunity for one and all.

SLAUGHTER AND MAY

www.slaughterandmay.com

Vacancies for around 90 graduates in 2011
For training contracts starting in 2013

 Law

Starting salary for 2011
£38,000

Universities that Slaughter and May plans to visit in 2010-11
Birmingham, Bristol, Cambridge, Durham, Edinburgh, Leeds, London, Manchester, Nottingham, Oxford, Warwick
Please check with your university careers service for details of events.

Application deadline
See website for full details.

Contact Details
✉ trainee.recruit@ slaughterandmay.com

Turn to page 248 now to request more information or visit our new website at www.top100graduateemployers.com

Slaughter and May is a leading international law firm whose principal areas of practice are in the fields of corporate, commercial and financing law.

The firm's clients range from the world's leading multinationals to venture capital start-ups. They include public and private companies, governments and non-governmental organisations, commercial and investment banks. The lawyers devise solutions for complex, often transnational, problems and advise some of the world's brightest business minds.

Their overseas offices and close working relationships with leading independent law firms in other jurisdictions mean there are opportunities to work in places such as Auckland, Brussels, Berlin, Copenhagen, Düsseldorf, Frankfurt, Helsinki, Hong Kong, Luxembourg, Madrid, Milan, New York, Oslo, Paris, Prague, Rome, Singapore, Stockholm, Sydney and Tokyo.

Approximately 90 training contracts are available per year for trainee solicitors. Slaughter and May also offers work experience schemes at Christmas, Easter and during the summer for those considering a career in law.

Following Law School, there is a two year training period during which time trainee solicitors gain experience of a broad cross-section of the firm's practice by taking an active part in the work of four or five groups, sharing an office with a partner or experienced associate. In addition, Slaughter and May offers an extensive training programme of lectures, seminars and courses with discussion groups covering general and specialised legal topics.

Applications from candidates of good 2.1 ability from any discipline are considered. Please visit the website for further information.

SLAUGHTER AND MAY

Great minds think differently

Slaughter and May is widely regarded as one of the most prestigious law firms in the world. Our lawyers are renowned for their sharp intellect, their attention to detail and their talent for finding innovative solutions to complex legal problems.

If you have an enquiring mind, the ability to think for yourself and a good 2:1 degree or better (not necessarily in law), then this could be the firm for you.

To find out more about career opportunities, visit **slaughterandmay.com**

SONY
make.believe

www.sony.eu/egp

Vacancies for around 10-15 graduates in 2011

- General Management
- Marketing
- Media
- Retailing
- Sales

Vacancies also available in Europe.

Starting salary for 2011
£Competitive

Universities that Sony plans to visit in 2010-11
Please check with your university careers service for details of events.

Application deadline
15th January 2011

Contact Details
✉ eurograd@eu.sony.com

Turn to page 248 now to request more information or visit our new website at www.top100graduateemployers.com

BUSINESS EXPERIENCE
Over the two years, our graduates rotate on two assignments taking roles in Sales, Marketing, Business Development and Finance.

TRAINING MODULES
Pan-European training modules are delivered by top management giving graduates a unique networking opportunity.

MENTORING PROGRAMME
Each graduate receives a mentor from the middle management Leadership Development Programme.

SOCIAL ENTREPRENEURSHIP
Graduates collaborate in groups and apply their business skills making a real contribution to a social project.

Sony is a leading global innovator of audio, video, communications and information technology products for both the consumer and professional markets. From electronics to media and entertainment, Sony is at the heart of global popular culture.

Sony is renowned for its audio-visual products, such as the BRAVIA™ 3D LCD TV, Cyber-shot™ digital camera, Handycam® camcorder and Walkman® MP3 player as well as its VAIO™ personal computers and high-definition (HD) professional broadcast equipment. Offering a complete end-to-end 3D HD value chain and with its electronics, music, pictures, game and online businesses, Sony is one of the world's leading digital entertainment brands, employing approximately 170,000 people worldwide.

The European Graduate Programme (EGP) from Sony is a two year high-potential programme which combines business experience, training modules, mentoring and social entrepreneurship. Benefiting from on-the-job and off-the-job development, EGP graduates collaborate on projects and contribute to current business strategy within experienced teams.

Sony EGP graduates generally have an excellent academic track record in a business-related degree or relevant business experience, such as internships or placements. Additionally, applicants are expected to be operational at a business level in three European languages. EGP applicants should be dedicated and flexible enough to follow the exciting opportunities of their journey within Sony. Operating in a global marketplace, Sony is looking for the next generation of internationally-minded players who are prepared to be mobile across Europe.

For more information on the EGP go to: www.sony.eu/egp

do

build

design

imagine

spirit

SONY
make.believe

dream

action

think

European Graduate Programme

To apply go to www.sony.eu/egp

Believe that anything you can imagine, you can make real.

BUSINESS EXPERIENCE

TRAINING MODULES

MENTORING PROGRAMME

SOCIAL ENTREPRENEURSHIP

European Graduate Programme

TeachFirst

www.teachfirst.org.uk

**Vacancies for around
730 graduates in 2011**

■ All Sectors

Starting salary for 2011
£Competitive

**Universities Teach First
plans to visit in 2010-11**

Aston, Bath, Birmingham,
Bristol, Brunel, Cambridge,
Cardiff, Durham, Edinburgh,
Exeter, Glasgow, Lancaster,
Leeds, Leicester, Liverpool,
London, Loughborough,
Manchester, Newcastle,
Nottingham, Oxford,
Sheffield, Southampton,
St Andrews, Surrey, Sussex,
Warwick, York
Please check with your university
careers service for details of events.

Application deadline
Winter: 6th December 2010
Final: 18th April 2011

Contact Details

✉ faq@teachfirst.org.uk

☎ 020 3117 2498

Turn to page 248 now to request more
information or visit our new website at
www.top100graduateemployers.com

It's time to make a difference – to invest in changing lives and achieving something lasting. Energy, intelligence and creativity can transform the futures of students and drive up standards in challenging schools around the UK.

Teach First is a charity that provides the training and support to enable high-calibre graduates to make a real impact in addressing one of the UK's most damaging social issues, educational disadvantage. At the same time, while they are transforming the lives of young people in schools around the country, Teach First helps graduates to dramatically enhance their own career potential and become part of a movement that is effecting profound change throughout the UK.

Teach First offers an exceptional leadership development programme that focuses on education, and which includes in its first year a PGCE qualification. With high-quality training, supportive coaching and ongoing alumni programmes, Teach First provides a unique platform of skills and experience to take forward into any future management career. That's why over 80 companies, government agencies and public bodies back Teach First's ability to effect change and to develop top talent for the future.

Put simply, graduates who can engage, manage and inspire a class of under-performing teenagers can handle pretty well any situation in any business. Few other options offer the same degree of genuine responsibility so early. And rarely, if ever, will graduates have the opportunity to make such a direct and important impact.

Teach First is a chance to join in, and to stand out. When it offers so much, the real question is, 'Why not Teach First?'

SARA
RICHARDSON
SCIENCE

REBECCA
WHITE
HISTORY

VISHAL
PARMAR
MATHS

JASON
ARTHUR
ENGLISH

TAMSIN
ROBINSON
GEOGRAPHY

JONATHAN
SOBCZYK
CITIZENSHIP

Join in, stand out,
Teach First.

Registered charity no: 1098294

Question:
A class in a challenging school has 32 pupils.
13 of them are eligible for free school meals.
How many of them will go on to attend university?

Answer:
Just 2.

Is that ok with you? It's not with us — and we're doing something about it.
Over 2,500 outstanding graduates — people like you — have joined us and
become exceptional teachers and leaders, and transformed the life chances
of young people in challenging schools.

Now it's your turn.

TeachFirst

www.teachfirst.org.uk

TESCO

www.tesco-graduates.com

Vacancies for around 200 graduates in 2011

- Accountancy
- Consulting
- Engineering
- Finance
- Human Resources
- IT
- Logistics
- Marketing
- Purchasing
- Retailing

Starting salary for 2011
£Competitive

Universities that Tesco plans to visit in 2010-11
Bristol, Cambridge, London, Loughborough, Manchester, Nottingham Trent, Oxford, Reading
Please check with your university careers service for details of events.

Application deadline
See website for full details.

Contact Details
✉ graduate.recruitment@uk.tesco.com
Turn to page 248 now to request more information or visit our new website at www.top100graduateemployers.com

Tesco is best known as the UK's number one retailer – a worldwide brand with a £62.5billion turnover. As the largest private sector employer, it's no surprise that Tesco are also recognised for their fantastic graduate opportunities.

But there's a lot more to Tesco. Something people may not realise is they're a pioneer in greener retailing: they have reduced carrier bag usage by three billion and last year were rated the 15th greenest company in the UK. What's more, Tesco opened the world's first zero-carbon supermarket in Ramsey, Cambridgeshire in December 2009.

For graduates, this innovation means they'll be joining a forward-thinking company that takes corporate social responsibility seriously – much like the development of their graduates. In fact, Tesco offers a total of 17 diverse graduate programmes that each provide huge scope for progression. Whether graduates want to begin their career in, to name a few, property, customer analysis, stores or distribution, Tesco's breadth of graduate programmes has it covered.

Depending on the area they join, graduates get involved in anything from sourcing products, to negotiating prices with suppliers, and predicting sales forecasts for acquiring land. Within three to five years, graduates can even be running their own store. In other words, Tesco's structured fast-track programmes offer outstanding rewards and development.

Tesco looks for ambitious graduates from any discipline who have the drive to succeed and understand the importance of delivering for the customer, whatever part of the business they work in.

Success. Sustained.

With 472,000 staff, stores in 14 countries and a total sales increase of over 50% during the past 5 years, it would be difficult to miss our business growth. Even our broccoli sales now weigh in at 450 tonnes a week in the UK.

But what may have passed you by is our growth as a green and sustainable business too. From getting our Tesco train on track delivering supplies by rail, to supporting farmers by buying localchoice milk, we're cutting our CO_2 emissions more and more each day. We're even saving 20,000 tonnes of cardboard by delivering products in reusable plastic trays. Come and help us sustain our success, visit **www.tesco-graduates.com**

Graduate Programmes:

Buying
Corporate Affairs
Corporate Marketing
Customer Analysis
Distribution Management
Finance
Human Resources
Merchandising
Product Technology

Property (Includes: Construction & Development , Design, Engineering and Product Display & Space Management)
Site Research
Store Management
Supply Chain
Technology Leadership
Tesco.com
Tesco Telecoms
UK Support Office

www.tesco-graduates.com

Tesco is an equal opportunities employer.

TESCO | *Every little helps*

Transport for London

www.tfl.gov.uk/graduates

Vacancies for around 50 graduates in 2011

- Accountancy
- Engineering
- Finance
- General Management
- IT
- Logistics
- Purchasing

Starting salary for 2011
£25,000

Universities that Transport for London plans to visit in 2010-11

Bath, Bristol, Brunel, Cambridge, City, Leeds, London, Loughborough, Nottingham, Oxford, Sheffield, Southampton, Warwick
Please check with your university careers service for details of events.

Application deadline
Varies by function
See website for full details.

Contact Details

✉ questions@tflgraduates.co.uk
☎ 0844 543 9739

Turn to page 248 now to request more information or visit our new website at www.top100graduateemployers.com

> London brings the world together in one city.
>
> *Boris Johnson*

Transport for London (TfL) has a huge part to play in making London what it is. The Tube, the trains, the buses, the river, the roads, the trams, the DLR, the taxis, the cycle lanes – TfL is responsible for virtually every mode of transport in the city.

The graduates that join TfL will enjoy just as much impact on the Capital. They could explore engineering or finance; procurement or management; transport planning or project management; quantity surveying or IM.

They might find themselves running an entire Underground station; examining how London's transport infrastructure fits together; or putting a project into place that could radically change how people travel across the city. TfL certainly doesn't shy away from giving their graduates heavy responsibility, very early on.

In fact, there's a great deal graduates could be influencing. Right now, TfL is in the midst of one of the greatest periods of investment in its history. Low-carbon taxis are being introduced. Buses are being redesigned. A cycling revolution is underway. The Tube is being comprehensively upgraded. New railways are being created. Plus, of course, the 2012 Games are on their way.

Whichever opportunity graduates choose, and whatever they turn their talent to, they can expect support, training and responsibility worthy of one of London's largest employers. These are unique opportunities for people with the flair, potential and personality to make a vital contribution to one of the world's greatest cities.

The world is but a canvas to the imagination.

Henry David Thoreau

Leave your mark on London – become a TfL graduate.

We want to be as diverse as the city we represent and welcome applications from everyone regardless of age, gender, ethnicity, sexual orientation, faith or disability.

tfl.gov.uk/tt100

MAYOR OF LONDON

Transport for London

www.ubs.com/graduates

Vacancies for around 500+ graduates in 2011

- Accountancy
- Finance
- Human Resources
- Investment Banking
- IT

Vacancies also available in Europe, the USA and Asia.

Starting salary for 2011
£Competitive

Universities that UBS plans to visit in 2010-11

Aston, Bath, Bristol, Cambridge, City, London, Loughborough, Manchester, Nottingham, Oxford, Warwick
Please check with your university careers service for details of events.

Application deadline
Varies by function
See website for full details.

Contact Details
✉ sh-ubs-campusrecruiting
@ubs.com

Turn to page 248 now to request more information or visit our new website at www.top100graduateemployers.com

UBS is one of the world's top financial firms, specialising in investment banking, wealth management and asset management. With offices in over 50 countries, the firm provides a variety of products and services to clients around the globe, including blue-chip companies, governments and wealthy individuals.

UBS recruits graduates from all academic backgrounds – the humanities and sciences, as well as economics and finance. Because of its global reach, the firm is particularly keen to hear from students with strong language skills. For UBS, degree subject is less important than a graduate's ability to prove they can analyse problems, plan ahead, make decisions, demonstrate sound judgement, and communicate with others. The other qualities UBS seeks in graduates are ambition, integrity, a commitment to accuracy, and a desire to work as part of a friendly but driven team.

UBS's Graduate Training Programme offers talented graduates 18-24 months of continuous learning in a fast-paced but supportive environment. The programme lays the foundation for a rewarding career in finance by combining intensive classroom education, coaching from more senior colleagues and on-the-job experience in a variety of teams.

Graduates and interns who have spent time at UBS say the firm has a particular culture that makes it different from other players in the industry. That culture stems from UBS's belief that business success is grounded in strong relationships with clients and real teamwork between colleagues. It makes UBS's people great to work with and the firm the choice of clients the world over.

© UBS 2010. All rights reserved.

Want a fulfilling career that rewards *energy and fresh* thinking? That's what we want too.

Looking for a career where your ideas could really make a difference? UBS's Graduate Programme and internships are a chance for you to experience for yourself what it's like to be part of a global team that rewards your input and believes in succeeding together. Wherever you are in your academic career, make your future a part of ours by visiting www.ubs.com/graduates.

UBS is an Equal Opportunity Employer. We respect and seek to empower each individual and the diverse cultures, perspectives, skills and experiences within our workforce.

www.ubs.com/graduates

Unilever

www.unilever.co.uk/careers

Vacancies for around 40 graduates in 2011

- Engineering
- Finance
- Human Resources
- IT
- Manufacturing
- Marketing
- Research & Development
- Sales

Starting salary for 2011
£26,500

Universities that Unilever plans to visit in 2010-11

Aston, Bath, Belfast, Birmingham, Bristol, Cambridge, Durham, Edinburgh, Exeter, Lancaster, Leeds, Liverpool, London, Loughborough, Manchester, Newcastle, Nottingham, Oxford, Sheffield, Strathclyde, Surrey, Warwick, York
Please check with your university careers service for details of events.

Application deadline
See website for full details.

Contact Details
✉ enquiry@unilevergraduates.com
☎ 0870 154 3550

Turn to page 248 now to request more information or visit our new website at www.top100graduateemployers.com

Unilever, a leading consumer goods company, makes some of the world's best-loved brands: Dove, Ben & Jerry's, PG Tips, Persil, and Marmite to name just a few. Across the world, Unilever is inspired to help people look good, feel good and get more out of life. That's why 150 million times a day, someone somewhere chooses a Unilever product.

Today, Unilever's ambition is to develop new ways of doing business that ensure it doubles in size, while reducing its environmental impact. Behind that ambition, and every single brand, lie many exciting challenges.

Unilever's Future Leaders Programme is designed to help graduates reach senior management. Graduates join a specific function, where they enjoy very real responsibilities from the outset. Generally, the two-year scheme includes a number of placements in various locations, so flexibility is essential to achieve the breadth of experience needed to succeed. Excellent training covers everything from leadership development to general business and professional skills. Full support is also offered to gain Chartered status or relevant professional qualifications, such as CIMA, IMechE, IChemE, IEE and CIPD.

Unilever has always believed in the power of its brands to improve the quality of people's lives. Successful applicants will be the driving force behind them. Graduates who succeed at Unilever are passionate about business, inspired by profit, competition and customer satisfaction, as well as have the ability to behave with integrity showing both ambition and entrepreneurial spirit. Unilever's high-quality training programmes help graduates develop the expertise and personal qualities needed to achieve the highest aspirations. Whatever the ambition, graduates can fulfil it at Unilever.

FOR WANT OF A BETTER WORLD

At Unilever, you'll discover an organisation that's committed to a new way of doing business. Voted number one in the Food Sector of the Dow Jones Sustainability Index for the last 11 years, we're winning the accolades that prove it. We're dedicated to improving life for colleagues, customers and communities across the world. By inspiring people to take small everyday actions that can add up to a big difference, we're embarking on a journey that will see us double our size while reducing our environmental impact. That means you get to make our global brands even better – as well as the recognition that you're making a positive difference to the planet.

Join Unilever as a graduate and you'll have a real job with real responsibility from day one. If you succeed in the programme, after two years you'll have your first management position. How's that for a chance to show the world what you can do? The nature of our work means you'll need to think globally. You'll also need the ability to take brands that are loved by millions and make them perform even better. We've opportunities in **Marketing, Supply Chain, Research & Development, Customer Development, Business & Technology Management, HR** and **Financial Management**. Find out more and apply via our website.

Could it be

WANT MORE VISIT UNILEVER.CO.UK/CAREERS

www.vodafone.co.uk/discoveruk

Vacancies for around
50 graduates in 2011

Engineering

Finance

Human Resources

IT

Marketing

Retailing

Sales

Starting salary for 2011
£25,000

Universities Vodafone plans to visit in 2010-11
Please check with your university careers service for details of events.

Application deadline
End of January 2011

Contact Details
Turn to page 248 now to request more information or visit our new website at www.top100graduateemployers.com

Vodafone UK is part of the world's leading mobile telecommunications company, with 341 million customers in 31 countries around the world.

After six years, Vodafone successfully returned to the graduate market last year and is now looking for future leaders to join their 2011 UK Graduate Programme.

Graduates will need a 2:1 undergraduate degree (in any subject) or a merit in a postgraduate degree and be ready to start early September 2011. Those who are internet-savvy, have a healthy competitive streak and are up for a challenge will have the opportunity to prove themselves during the 12 month programme.

On the programme, graduates will get to experience two months within a retail store. The remainder of the programme will be spent working within two other UK-based departments that complement their skills and ambitions.

During the programme graduates can expect a full induction, training, development and support. Additionally, they will be able to access a host of courses, online learning and group activities.

At the end of the year, there's the chance to secure a full-time position for those who possess the energy, talent and customer obsession required.

Graduates unsuccessful in securing a role will have gained from the valuable experience of working at the heart of one of the world's biggest consumer brands.

Those who are successful can look forward to being offered a permanent role and an exciting career at Vodafone.

12 months, 3 roles, 1 chance to shine

A graduate programme like no other

If you have (or are expecting) a 2:1 in any subject, or a merit in your postgraduate degree – and are ready to start in September 2011 – visit www.vodafone.co.uk/discoveruk to apply today.

power to you

vodafone

WPP

Vacancies for around 1-10 graduates in 2011

- Marketing
- Media

Vacancies also available in the USA, Asia and elsewhere in the world.

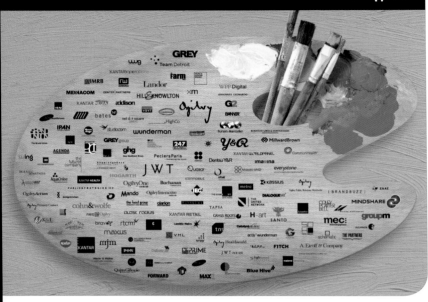

Starting salary for 2011
£Competitive

Universities that WPP plans to visit in 2010-11
Bristol, Cambridge, Edinburgh, London, Nottingham, Oxford, Warwick
Please check with your university careers service for details of events.

Application deadline
11th November 2010

Contact Details
✉ hmiller@wpp.com
☎ 020 7408 2204

Turn to page 248 now to request more information or visit our new website at www.top100graduateemployers.com

WPP is the world leader in communications services, made up of leading companies in advertising; media investment management; consumer insight; public relations & public affairs; branding & identity; healthcare communications; direct, digital, promotion & relationship marketing; and specialist communications.

WPP companies provide communications services to clients worldwide including 354 of the Fortune Global 500, 28 of the Dow Jones 30, 60 of the NASDAQ 100 and 33 of the Fortune e-50. Collectively, WPP employs 138,000 people (including associates) in almost 2,400 offices in 107 countries.

WPP Marketing Fellowships develop high-calibre management talent with experience across a range of marketing disciplines. WPP is offering several three-year, unique multi-disciplinary experience Fellowships, with competitive remuneration and excellent long term career prospects within WPP.
Each year of the Fellowship is spent working in a WPP sponsoring company and a personal mentor is assigned to provide overall career guidance.
Each rotation is chosen on the basis of the individual's interests and the Group's needs.

Fellowships will be awarded to applicants who are intellectually curious and motivated by the prospect of delivering high-quality communications services to their clients. WPP wants people who are committed to marketing, take a rigorous and creative approach to problem-solving, are intellectually curious and will function well in a flexible, loosely structured work environment.

All applicants should have completed an undergraduate degree (class 2:1 or above) or equivalent.

WPP
Marketing Fellowships 2011

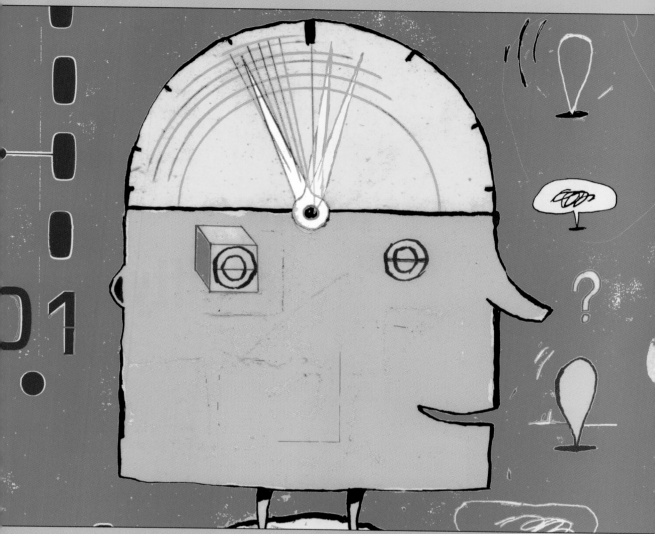

Ambidextrous brains required

WPP is the world leader in communications services. Major brands include JWT, Ogilvy & Mather Worldwide, Y&R, Grey, United, Mindshare, MEC, MediaCom, Millward Brown, Kantar Media, OgilvyOne Worldwide, Wunderman, OgilvyAction, Hill & Knowlton, Ogilvy Public Relations Worldwide, Burson-Marsteller, Cohn & Wolfe, CommonHealth, Sudler & Hennessey, TNS, Ogilvy Healthworld, ghg, The Brand Union, Landor, Fitch and G2 among others.

Their specialist skills include Advertising; Media Investment Management; Consumer Insight; Public Relations & Public Affairs; Branding & Identity; Healthcare Communications; Direct, Digital, Promotion & Relationship Marketing; and Specialist Communications. They are all in business to contribute to the success of their clients. And they do so through a demanding combination of flair and slog; intuition and logic; left brain and right brain.

We are looking for people who are intellectually curious and motivated by the prospect of delivering high-quality communications services to their clients. Those selected will work in a number of WPP companies and across different marketing disciplines. Excellent long-term career prospects within a WPP company.

Deadline for entry: 11 November 2010
Visit our website and apply online at www.wpp.com

Information leaflets are available from:
Harriet Miller at WPP, 27 Farm Street, London W1J 5RJ
T +44(0)20 7408 2204 F +44(0)20 7493 6819
E-mail: hmiller@wpp.com

Enter our prize draw to win

£5,000 or one of 500 books or fifty £50 iTunes vouchers!

Make use of our free information service to find out more about the employers featured within this edition of **The Times Top 100 Graduate Employers,** and you could be £5,000 richer when you start your first job!

All you need to do is complete the special *Top 100* **Information Request** card opposite and send it back before the final closing date, **31st March 2011.** Or you can register online now at **www.Top100GraduateEmployers.com**

The first 500 entries will receive a free copy of *The Graduate Jobs Formula* book, by Dr Paul Redmond.

Every completed request card or online registration will be entered into a special prize draw to win £5,000 in cash.

There are also **fifty £50 iTunes vouchers** to be won – one at each of the universities at which the *Top 100* book is distributed, for those who reply by **30th November 2010.**

Once registered, you'll receive regular email updates with news and information about the employers you're interested in.

This service is entirely free to all UK students and recent graduates.

Fill in the card or go to www.Top100GraduateEmployers.com now!

Terms and Conditions for the Prize Draw - 1. Entry to this Prize Draw will be on receipt of a completed 'Information Request' card or registering online at www.Top100GraduateEmployers.com   2. Entries are limited to one per person, no purchase necessary.   3. The Prize Draw is open to all UK residents aged 18 or over who are studying on or are a recent graduate from a full-time degree course at a UK university or college of higher education. Employees of High Fliers Publications Ltd, Times Newspapers Ltd, its associated companies or agents directly associated with this Prize Draw are not eligible to enter.   4. The Prize Draw will take place on 4th April 2011 under independent supervision and the winner will be notified in writing. No correspondence will be entered into concerning this Prize Draw.   5. The first entry drawn will receive £5,000.   6. The prize is not transferable. 7. The winner's entry to the Prize Draw assumes the winner consents to participation in High Fliers Publications Ltd and Times Newspapers Ltd promotional publicity about this Prize Draw.   8. The promoter is: High Fliers Publications Ltd, King's Gate, 1 Bravingtons Walk, London N1 9AE.